W9-AWU-643

THE
CICHLIDS
YEARBOOK

Volume 2

Ad Konings (Editor)

CICHLID PRESS

1		
2	3	4

Cover photographs:
1 - *Protomelas* sp. "Steveni Taiwan", Lake Malaŵi, Malaŵi.
2 - *Tilapia tholloni*, Alima River, Congo.
3 - *"Cichlasoma"* sp. "Labridens Tamasopo", Pánuco, México.
4 - *Tropheus moorii* (Murago), Lusingu, Lake Tanganyika, Zaïre.

Text and photographs by Ad Konings
except as otherwise indicated

Mary Bailey (Crediton, UK)
corrected the manuscript

The editor wants to thank the following persons who
supplied various cichlids for photographic purposes:
Peter Baasch (Stegen, Germany)
Marc Danhieux (Maltavi, Hohenahr-Erda, Germany)
Alain Gillot (Zaïre Cichlids, Kalemie, Zaïre)
Stuart Grant (Salima, Malaŵi)
René Krüter (Krüter Tropicals, Rotterdam, Netherlands)
Roland Numrich (Mimbon Aquarium, Köln, Germany)
Edwin Reitz (Aquapport, Ronnenberg, Germany)
Dirk Verduijn (Verduyn Cichlids, Zevenhuizen,
Netherlands)

Distributors:

USA: Old World Exotic Fish, Inc., P.O.Box 970583, Miami, Florida 33197
UK: Animal House (U.K.), Ltd., QBM Business Park, Birstall, Batley, West Yorkshire WF17 9QD
Sweden: Fohrman Aquaristik AB, Odds Väg 7, 433 75 Partille
France: Africa, 9 Place Duberry, 92390 Villeneuve La Garenne
Germany: Aquapport (Edwin Reitz), Köselstraße 20, 3003 Ronnenberg
Netherlands: NVC, Lieshoutseweg 31, 5708 CW Stiphout

ISBN 3-928457-05-5

Copyright© 1992. Cichlid Press. All rights reserved.
No part of this publication may be reproduced, stored in a retrieval system, or transmitted in any form or by any
means − electronic, mechanical, photocopying, recording or otherwise − without the prior permission of the authors,
and the publisher.

Cichlid Press, Blütenweg 17, 6837 St. Leon-Rot, Germany

Printed by RAKET B.V., Pijnacker, Holland

The CICHLIDS yearbook

CONTENTS

The CICHLIDS yearbook

Introduction

No less than eighteen authors have put together the second volume of the cichlids yearbook. It was pleasing that almost all contributors to the first volume were able to write down another piece of their knowledge and experience in this one. In addition eight new authors have written for this volume. Another pleasing fact is that Horst Walter Dieckhoff (Lake Fish, Herten, Germany), the famous underwater photographer, is back in "cichlid-business". For this volume he has provided some of his photographs but we have made some plans for the near future.....

The "new" authors are briefly introduced in the same order as their articles appear:

Hans-Joachim Herrmann (Hamburg, Germany), a Tanganyika specialist and known for his book on these cichlids, describes two new variants of *Simochromis*, which he has collected himself.

Another book-author and Malaŵi specialist, Dr. Andreas Spreinat (Göttingen, Germany), deals with the genus *Cynotilapia* and relates his experience with some other cichlids as well.

Edwin Reitz (Aquapport, Ronnenberg, Germany), a professional and very experienced cichlid breeder, describes the breeding procedure of *Aulonocara rostratum*.

Recently the first commercial shipments of fish from Lake Nyasa, as Lake Malaŵi is known in Tanzania, have been exported from that country. Two independent operations have been started. In the next volume we will have some more species for you but this time Peter Knabe (Schlangen, Germany), who visited one of the exporters in Liuli, Tanzania, describes his observations on a beautiful *Labidochromis* from that region.

The Victorian cichlids receive more attention in this volume. Ole Seehausen (Hannover, Germany), who is a scientist working in Tanzania in the Haplochromis Ecology Survey Team and thus has first-hand experience, has contributed his first installment.

Jan 't Hooft (Hendrik Ido Ambacht, Netherlands), a lifetime aquarist and the founder of the Dutch cichlid association, tells us about one of his passions, namely *Tilapia*.

Do you keep mbuna with larger Malaŵian haplochromines in your tank? Then you know that at feeding time the mbuna devour the major part of the food. It usually takes them ten seconds to do so. Roger Häggström (Örnsköldsvik, Sweden), the editor of Ciklid Bladet, the periodical of the Swedish cichlid association, tells us how we can keep the mbuna busy eating.

Last but not at all the least in the long row of "new" authors, Mary Bailey (Crediton, UK) explains how scientists (should) give names to fish. Mary, who has been on the committee of the British Cichlid Association since 1982 and has studied English and Latin, was also of tremendous help in correcting the manuscripts of the yearbooks. She has kept and bred many species and is an aquaristic consultant for several aquarium magazines in the UK.

A very important publication has been issued recently, namely *Cichlid Fishes; Behaviour, Ecology and Evolution*. It is the cichlid bible for the years to come for every aquarist interested in cichlids. It is discussed by Martin Geerts.

In the previous volume I have reported on *Neolamprologus leloupi* and said that *N. caudopunctatus* should be regarded as a synonym of this species. However, when I visited the locality in Zaïre where the yellow-dorsalled cichlid is collected, it was immediately clear that I was wrong: both species, *N. caudopunctatus* and *N. leloupi*, live sympatrically in the same habitat. I further explain the situation on page 21.

With regard to Willem Heijns' contribution in volume 1 about *"Cichlasoma" spinosissimum*, Jaap-Jan de Greef (Parrish, Florida), who re-discovered this species for the hobby, wrote me that he found the species in pools at the southern end of Lago de Izabal but not in the lake itself. Jaap-Jan collects fish in Central America and Africa and breeds them for a hobby.

Without the hospitality and cooperation of several exporters and friends it would not have been possible to show you the cichlids in their natural habitat and give information on how they live. I therefore gratefully acknowledge Stuart M. Grant (Salima, Malaŵi), Alain Gillot (Zaïre Cichlids, Kalemie, Zaïre), Gary Kratochvil (San Antonio, Texas), Juan Miguel Artigas Azas (San Luis Potosí, México) and Mireille Schreyen (Fishes of Burundi, Burundi).

Ad Konings

TANGANYIKAN CICHLIDS

Clues to a step-wise speciation

This race of *Ophthalmotilapia ventralis* at M'Toto, Zaïre closely resembles that from Cape Mpimbwe, Tanzania (see page 7).

Among the many endemic species of cichlids in Lake Tanganyika which are known to date, there are a number of species which have evolved geographical races. The best known examples of such cichlids are the species of the *Tropheus*-complex. Many different geographical variants have been found which all seem to belong to five, maybe six, species. Besides *Tropheus* there are other species like *Cyathopharynx furcifer* and *Ophthalmotilapia ventralis* which have evolved several different races. Not only the mouth-brooders among the cichlids have formed distinct populations but also substrate-spawners

like *Neolamprologus caudopunctatus* and *N. leloupi* (for the latter species see page 21).
Recently, Martin Geerts and I made a short expedition along the southern Zaïrean coast from Kalemie to Moliro. It was our intention to make a preliminary inventory of the rock-dwelling cichlids in this part of the lake. During our trip we became aware of a remarkable feature which may have a greater impact on the theory of speciation than our first observations indicated. We observed geographically isolated populations of species whose coloration had a remarkable resemblance to populations along the opposite

side of the lake. We knew about these populations through the many photographs made by Walter Dieckhoff in the Tanzanian part of the lake.

Ophthalmotilapia ventralis inhabits the southern half of the lake and is known in about a dozen distinguishable colour varieties, each geographically isolated. On the Tanzanian coast at Cape Mpimbwe lives a race which is characterized by a black-blue ground colour with an irregular, broad white band running diagonally across the body (photo this page).

Between Cape Tembwe and the bay of Zongwe on the Zaïrean coast an almost identical variant of *O. ventralis* is found (see photo page 6).

bottom). In the Zambian part, however, another race inhabits the intermediate and sandy biotopes (see photo page 89).

The geographical variant of *T. moorii* found between Moba and Zongwe closely resembles the small population at Kibwesa, Tanzania (see Konings, 1990 *TFH* 39 (3): 71) while the race found at Kapampa (see photo page 9) shows a strong resemblance to the race near Mpulungu. The latter two populations, however, are separated by a long shoreline which is inhabited by about a dozen different other variants.

T. polli has been described from the central Tanzanian coast and is characterized by having four spines in the anal fin, a feature it shares,

Ophthalmotilapia ventralis at Cape Mpimbwe, Tanzania. Photo by Walter Dieckhoff.

Further south along the coast a yellow race of *O. ventralis* inhabits the shallow rocky biotope. The race found at Kapampa closely resembles that found at Kipili, Tanzania (Konings, 1988: 61). At Lupota, Zaïre, the variant shows more yellow pigment and is almost identical with that found at Malasa Island, Tanzania.

Cyathopharynx furcifer is known from most locations around the lake and about six different races are known. The race found along most of the southern part of the Zaïrean coast (see photo page 8 top) is practically identical to the one on the other side of the lake (see photo page 8

among its congeners, only with *T. annectens*. Other *Tropheus* have 5 to 7 spines. At M'Toto, Zaïre, I observed *T. annectens* in its habitat and found no apparent difference in behaviour or morphology to that of *T. polli*.

Neolamprologus leloupi occurs on both sides of the lake (in the southern half) but is not found in Zambia. On page 21 some of its affinities with *N. caudopunctatus* are discussed. Both at Kapampa, Zaïre (see photo page 21) and at Kalambo, Tanzania/Zambia (René Krüter, pers. comm.) an identical race of *N. caudopunctatus* —which is not known to occur anywhere else — lives sympatrical-

7

Cyathopharynx furcifer, a male photographed south of Moba, Zaïre.

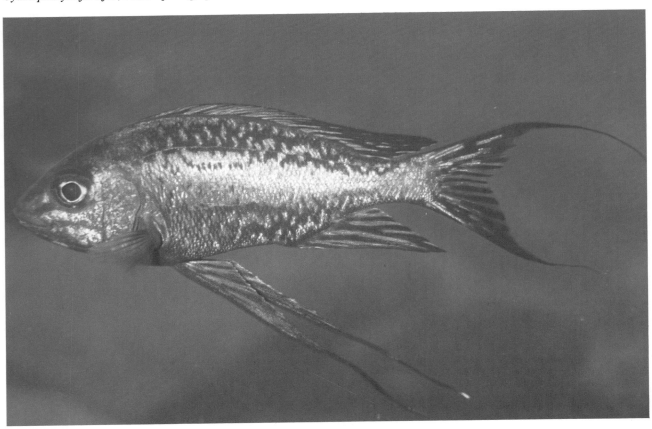

Cyathopharynx furcifer at Kipili, Tanzania. Photo by Walter Dieckhoff.

ly with *N. leloupi* at the borderline of both species' distribution.

There are several other species which have similar (not identical as in the previous examples) populations on both sides of the lake, e.g. *N. sexfasciatus*, several species of the *N. brichardi*-complex and *Chalinochromis* sp. "Popelini" in Zaïre and *C.* sp. "Bifrenatus" in Tanzania.

With regard to the following discussion, it is important to realize that *different* races of the species mentioned inhabit the Zambian waters. The first question one asks is how come such isolated populations look so much alike when it is known that they can develop many other colour patterns as well. The east and west coasts in the southern part of the lake are separated by the deepest water found in Africa. If one is conversant with the current theories about the fluctuations in lake levels since the origin of the lake, one can easily imagine a period in which the water dropped to a level which was low enough to connect parts of opposite coasts. In such small paleo-lakes the aforementioned species could have been present as a single geographical population. The rising water caused the fish to move upwards in order to keep up with the suitable habitat (vertical migration). This eventually resulted in the populations on either side becoming isolated. This seems to me the only plausible way to explain apparently identical races at both sides of the lake.

If this is indeed the only reasonable explanation then its implications are very important. During the low water stand there was no water in the Zambian area. Therefore all Zambian populations must have developed from individuals from the more northerly regions (horizontal migration). The fact that they almost all have a different colour pattern leads to the conclusion that these races must have developed in Zambian waters. We may then further conclude that speciation takes place mainly during the initial development of a new population. This, however, is at variance with Darwin's theory that evolution is a continuous process whereby new species are slowly generated.

Combining the existence of the similar variants on both sides of the lake with the widely accepted theory of the fluctuations in lake level, one can only envisage a step-wise evolution in the case of Tanganyikan cichlids. This hypothesis is further supported by the "fact" that during the development of the new populations in the southern part of the lake (while the water level rose) the old populations did not change at all!

These rather basic observations may lead us to conclude that when the bulk of the individuals of

Tropheus moorii at Kapampa, Zaïre.

a population remain together in one large breeding group, the cichlids of that group will not change, probably not in a million years! But when a drastic change does occur and new populations are founded, a new species could be developed almost overnight.

One could envisage the development of a new population as follows. As the rising water level opens up a new, *suitable*, habitat, wanderers from a nearby population could cross uninhabitable areas and settle at the new location (horizontal migration). Of course not just one species would occur at such a new site but many different species would found a new population. When such new populations are founded by small numbers of individuals then there is a statistical chance that a new colour variant will develop (interbreeding). Important factors in the development of a new race are, firstly, the number of wanderers founding the new population. Secondly, the constitution of the local fauna and the local circumstances may greatly influence the success of a particular species. The latter two factors probably act as catalysts in speciation and the development of a new variant may depend solely on the number of individuals at the site.

When a balance between the available species, number of individuals, and available niches has been established "evolution" is suspended until a new major change occurs in this habitat.

Acknowledgement

I was greatly stimulated by the discussions I enjoyed with Martin Geerts and Mary Bailey. I sincerely thank Alain Gillot of Zaïre Cichlids for giving us the opportunity to make a survey along the Zaïrean coast.

Spawning *Xenotilapia spiloptera* Poll & Stewart, 1975

The genus *Xenotilapia* can be divided into two groups; one group consists of maternal mouthbrooders and the other of species which form pairs during the breeding period and which employ the biparental mouthbrooding technique. However, this subdivision may not always be as clear-cut as is stated here (see page 18, Mark Smith's article about *X. ornatipinnis*).

X. spiloptera belongs to the group of biparental mouthbrooders. The holotype of this species was collected at Nkumbula Island near Mpulungu in Zambia, but its distribution seems to spread along other parts of Zambia and along the Zaïrean and Tanzanian shores.

During the breeding period *X. spiloptera* is intermingle with other species to form larger schools but most often groups consisting only of *X. spiloptera* are observed.

With the approach of the breeding season —at present it is not known whether there is a regular annual breeding season, or whether breeding is triggered by the effect of some external stimulus on the members of the school— the school moves closer to the rocky habitat and splits up into pairs. Each pair stays in a territory which is defended mainly against conspecifics.

The pair bond is established by repeated courtship displays by the male as well as by the female. In the artificial environment of the aquarium it seems that the bond between the pair

A mouthbrooding female *Xenotilapia spiloptera* from Kipili, Tanzania.

restricted to the rocky habitat. This has led to the existence of several geographical races. Most races have a colorless dorsal fin with some black markings on its edge. The race at Kigoma has a dorsal fin with tiny colored spots but lacking the blotchy markings found in all other known populations. The races inhabiting the rocky shores near Kipili in Tanzania have an attractive yellow coloration in addition to the black markings on the dorsal fin.

When not breeding, *X. spiloptera* sometimes lives in large schools over the sand. Here it forages by sifting the substrate for something edible. It may

is strengthened by the continuous protection of the territory. If only one pair is kept in the tank there is a risk that the male and female will quarrel and that one of them, not always the female, might end up cowering in one of the tank's corners. Even when the pair is not brooding, male and female stay together in a relatively small area.

The four pairs I keep in an 800 litre aquarium are each satisfied with an area about 30 cm in diameter. When one pair decides to spawn, it defends an area about double that size. It is difficult to predict an imminent spawning but

The female has just laid some eggs; the male waits behind her.

mutual courtship increases noticeably, sometimes days before the actual spawning. A slight change in the color pattern occurs as well; female as well as male acquires black markings in the upper and lower part of the iris. These, together with the pigment in the eye, form a black vertical bar across the eyeball. I don't know if this is a sign of readiness to spawn, but it is seen mostly when the pair is engaged in spawning or shortly before the act.

Spawning takes place inside the pair's territory but there is no specific site or nest where the eggs are deposited. In fact, the deposition site may change during spawning. In the maternal mouthbrooder group of *Xenotilapia*, male and female circle around each other before the eggs are laid, but *X. spiloptera* starts spawning when the female suddenly deposits some eggs on the substrate. I have never noticed a signal from the male for the female to start. He usually waits behind her, about 3 cm above the substrate, until she clears the site and leaves the eggs to be fertilized by him. While the male positions his vent over the eggs to fertilize them, the female turns around and waits until the male moves away. Then she picks up the eggs. The female will not lay any eggs if the male is not behind her. While he is chasing intruders from the territory she may remain at the site but she may also join the male in the territorial defence. After a short interruption the female again lowers her body to the substrate and waits for the male to take position behind her before she lays a new batch of eggs.

Spawns may be as large as 40 eggs but much seems to depend on the buccal capacity of the female. If the female's mouth is getting full she has to shuffle the eggs around before she can pick up new ones. Usually the male has his head near the eggs when the female collects them and sometimes picks up some eggs himself. Once I noticed that he picked up two eggs, which the female apparently didn't collect quickly enough,

The male fertilizes the eggs when they are on the substrate.

11

and swam away while chewing on them. Then the pair went through another cycle, and when the female wanted to pick up the new batch of eggs the male spat the two eggs in front of the female's mouth. They were immediately picked up by the female. During the next round, the female's mouth was probably too full and it took so long before she had arranged the eggs already inside her mouth that the male again took some eggs, but this time he ate them. The female didn't produce more eggs after this incident.

Shortly after spawning the pair reduces the territory to the usual 30 cm, but this is defended with more energy than usual. The first nine to twelve days the female broods the embryos and refrains from feeding. After this period the larvae are transferred to the male's mouth. I have never witnessed the procedure in its entirety but it is likely that, after a set ritual, the female spits all the larvae in front of the male's mouth. The male retrieves them quickly and continues the brooding for another ten days.

When the brooding is completed the male releases the fry in the territory where they are protected by both parents. For the first few days the fry may take refuge inside the male's mouth but most of the time they sit on the substrate. They sometimes wander off into other territories where they are protected by the resident pair. The fry measure about 15 mm at the time of release and it takes them about two years before they have reached the adult size of approximately 10 cm.

The biparental mouthbrooding technique is not more advanced than the maternal mouthbrooding procedure. While mouthbrooding pairs have to devote three to four weeks taking care of one brood, males of a maternal mouthbrooder can fertilize eggs of many females in the same period. In theory, this should not make a difference as long as there are as many females as males. The drawback of biparental mouthbrooding is the fact that a territory has to be maintained by the pair. In maternal mouthbrooders only the strongest males occupy a territory, and the mouthbrooding females gather in nursery schools. Where population density is high, as is the case in Lake Tanganyika, this offers a distinct advantage. Instead of having many territories spread over a large area, a species can propagate in a relatively small region of the biotope. Only the males have to worry about a territory and since there are fewer needed a loss during the selection process probably enhances the viability of the species.

The stimulus for the female of the biparental mouthbrooder to transfer the larvae to the male's mouth may be hunger. During the 9 to 12 days incubation she does not eat at all. Females of a maternal mouthbrooder endure a longer period without food but may eat small morsels in the second half of the incubation period. Such mouthbrooding females also exspend much less energy than those of a biparental mouthbrooder which also have to defend territory.

In Lake Tanganyika a maternal mouthbrooder is better off in several respects. This could explain the observation that breeding X. *spiloptera* are found at deeper levels of the biotope than are maternally mouthbrooding *Xenotilapia*. Breeding pairs are usually found at depths of between 15 and 40 meters

After fertilization the eggs are collected by the female.

The male watches the female picking up the eggs.

The genus *Tropheus*

The "Murago Moorii" exists in several variants. Here a male of the "Yellow Murago" collected near Zongwe, Zaïre

The species of the genus *Tropheus* have for many years been some of the most popular cichlids among aquarists. There are many hobbyists who keep exclusively *Tropheus* species. Although there are only six known species, at least four of these show great geographical variability. Fortunately most aquarists are aware of this fact and rarely house different variants of the same species in one tank. This would lead inevitably to bastardization.

The members of the genus *Tropheus* are usually well represented on most rocky coasts. Except for *T. duboisi*, they all inhabit the upper 10 metres of the biotope. Not only for their protection but also for their food, *Tropheus* species are restricted to areas with rocks. The feeding habits of *T. duboisi* have not been extensively investigated, but those of the other species have. *T. moorii, T. brichardi, T. polli* and *T.* sp. "Black" are all grazers which shear the filamentous algae from the rocky substrate (Yamaoka, 1983). *T. annectens*, which is restricted to the western, Zaïrean, shores of the lake, is closely related to and maybe even conspecific with *T. polli*, and behaves similarly to that species. It seems that *Tropheus* has a feeding relationship with several species of the genus *Petrochromis*. Members of the latter group, which are browsers combing unicellular diatoms from the algae strands, partially clear the biocover from

sediment and make it thus more suitable for *Tropheus* to feed on (Takamura, 1984).

In the artificial environment of the aquarium *T. moorii*, from the southern part of the lake, and *T.* sp. "Black", form the northern, behave as strongly territorial cichlids. Typically the largest males will divide the available space in the tank among themselves and leave the border areas of their territories as living space for females and weaker males. Territories in the aquarium measure more than 60 cm in diameter. In nature, the territoriality of these two species is not always as evident as it is in a tank. Although males have a territory where spawning takes place and in which they forage, conspecifics are not always chased from the premises. Sometimes we may observe a group of about 20 (*T.* sp. "Black") to 100 (*T. moorii*) individuals grazing on the same rock. In the wild, *T. brichardi* and *T. polli* are permanently territorial and, especially *T. brichardi*, are difficult to keep in small numbers in an aquarium.

Many aquarists have great interest in maintaining a breeding group of a particular variant of one of the species. Not only for the continuous interactions between the members of the group but also to spread the aggression of the most dominant males, it is advisable to have as large a group as possible. If each individual is given 25 to 40 litres of water a balanced breeding group can be established in a suitably decorated aquarium. Caves are not necessary as they will not provide shelter for harassed individuals; only the dominant males will occupy caves. Stones should be placed in such a way that clearly separate groups are created. Each group or heap of stones, if approximately 50 cm in diameter, will be regarded as a territory by a male and respected by the others.

Often more females are kept than males. This may work for most species of *Tropheus* but not always for *T. brichardi*. The latter species is best kept with as many males as females.

Before a group of *Tropheus* is introduced into the aquarium all of the fish must be in good condition or at least be in the same condition, and all of the fish must be introduced at the same time. The introduction of additional specimens to the group at a later stage must be avoided at all times! Newly introduced fish more often than not upset the established hierarchy in the group and frequently end up being chased by all other individuals. If the additional specimens are wild caught fishes which have not been quarantined long enough, an early death is generally the result. Currently this is the most important problem aquarists have maintaining *Tropheus*.

Wild caught fishes and fishes from aquaria in which wild caught specimens are housed have many different kinds of parasites. In the wild, these parasites live in balance with the host's immune system and are rarely present in harmful quantities. By virtue of the presence of a low number of parasites the host continuously maintains its resistance against an explosive increas in numbers of that parasite, although it never becomes totally immune. Fish in a healthy aquarium have very few parasites and thus mostly lack this semi-immunization. When a wild caught fish is introduced to an established group, it is immediately weakened by the repeated physical assaults it endures from all members of the group. This has a weakening effect on its immunity to parasites and a serious infestation is liable to result. Not only may the newly introduced fish die but the disease usually infects the non-resistant inhabitants as well. A single fish may thus completely wipe out a long established breeding colony. Therefore, **never** introduce untreated wild caught fish into a group of *Tropheus*. Several parasites are specific to a group of cichlids; they affect only those species while other species in the same aquarium do not show any sign of disease. Species that carry some of the *Tropheus*-affecting parasites are Goby Cichlids (*Eretmodus, Spathodus* and *Tanganicodus*), *Petrochromis, Simochromis,* and *Pseudosimochromis*.

A male *Tropheus brichardi* from the Kavalla Islands, Zaïre.

There are several ways of "cleaning" wild caught fish, but all of them involve a quarantine period.

A wild caught fish, living in balance with its parasite burden, can be cleansed of them by killing the existing parasite or by preventing re-infection where the parasites have left the fish in the course of their life cycle. To do this, however, one needs to know what organisms are involved. In *Tropheus* broad spectrum antibiotics and anti-parasitic solutions have had little effect in damming the spread of disease. What kills most *Tropheus* seems to be highly infectious agents, either virus or parasites. Many aquarists have tried numerous medicines to cure their fish, some with success. Reasoning tells us, however, that there may be several diseases involved and that thus one medicine will not automatically cure all fish.

As mentioned before, a fish may also be cured by preventing the parasite from re-infecting the host. If a parasite cannot find a host it will die. The infectious phase may live a long time but the agent infecting *Tropheus* seems to have a relatively short livespan. My personal experience and that of Hans Herrmann (pers. comm.) is that a biological trickle filter strongly inhibits the spreading of the disease. This can be explained by the fact that infectious parasites are carried away from the fish into the filtration system. It is our experience that water coming from the filter is free of pathogens. The faster the water is recycled through the trickle filter the more effectively it frees it from parasites. When the volume of water passed through the filter in one hour equals that of the tank's volume, an optimum treatment has been achieved. It is not known if faster cycles have a better or even the same effect. Slower cycles don't work that well.

So, wild caught fish could be cured by placing them in a quarantine tank which is filtered by a trickle filter; even when the tank is a part of a central filter system! It is important to leave the fish for at least two months on their own in that quarantine tank and have a separate hand-net for that tank only. When direct water-to-water contact with other tanks is avoided the result is healthy fish.

References

TAKAMURA, K. (1984) Interspecific relationships of aufwuchs-eating fishes in Lake Tanganyika. *Env. Biol. Fish.* 10 (4); pp 225-241.

YAMAOKA, K. (1983) Feeding behaviour and dental morphology of algae scraping cichlids (Pisces: Teleostei) in Lake Tanganyika. *Afr. Study Monogr.* 4; pp 77-89.

Tropheus sp. "Black", a geographical variant from Kiriza, Ubwari Peninsula, Zaïre.

Simochromis marginatus Poll, 1956

Hans-Joachim Herrmann

A wildcaught male *Simochromis marginatus* from Nyanza, Burundi. Photo by Hans-Joachim Herrmann.

Since its description 35 years ago, this cichlid has been known to the scientific world but has never been introduced into the aquaristic hobby. Its rather unexciting coloration could be one of the factors that postponed its entry into the hobby; on the other hand the first few specimens were only recently collected alive by some German aquarists.

Until then its only known occurrence was located on the northwestern coast of the lake, along the Zaïrean coastline. Now a second location has been found on the Burundi coast in the northeastern part, just north of Nyanza.

The fact that I discovered *Simochromis marginatus* in the rocky habitat at this location made me a little uneasy. This part of the lake, which is easily accessible, has been thoroughly investigated by the late Pierre Brichard. This author has denied, in his book "Cichlids and all the other fishes of Lake Tanganyika" (1989), the existence of *S. marginatus* in this part of the lake. My unease is increased by the fact that *S. margaretae* — this species has not yet been exported alive — is recorded from a location not far from the place where I found *S. marginatus*, i.e. Kigoma Bay. *S. margaretae* is also characterized by a black marginal band in the dorsal fin and has a very similar shape to *S. marginatus*.

Not until I had examined the specimens and compared them with the original descriptions of the two species could I conclude that I had collected *S. marginatus*. The only difference is the relatively deeper caudal peduncle of *S. margaretae*.

Like all other species of the genus *S. marginatus* spawns easily in captivity. The male constructs a shallow spawning-dish in the sand and leads ripe females with undulating and vibrating movements into his nest. When both partners are ready to spawn they circle the spawning-site. The eggs are fertilized inside the female's mouth. When all eggs are laid the female retreats from the male's territory and cares for the eggs during the following three weeks. After this period all egg yolk has been absorbed and the fry are about 1 cm long. Only when danger threatens are they taken back inside the female's mouth.

At a size of about 3 cm juvenile *S. marginatus* already show intraspecific aggression, and this is known to occur among the other species of the genus as well. Such aggression can easily be reduced by accompanying them with other non-related species like *Tropheus moorii* or a species of the genus *Petrochromis*.

Males can reach a maximum size of approximately 11 cm while females, which do not show a distinct black marginal band in the dorsal fin, remain about 2 cm smaller.

Simochromis babaulti Pellegrin, 1927

Hans-Joachim Herrmann

Simochromis babaulti; a submissive male is visible in the background. Photos by Hans-Joachim Herrmann.

The genus *Simochromis* consists of small to medium sized mouthbrooding cichlids which inhabit the rocky shallows or the intermediate biotopes in Lake Tanganyika.

One of the smaller species is *Simochromis babaulti* which has a maximum length of about 10 cm and which is fairly well known among aquarists. Because of its rather aggressive —intraspecific— behaviour, and its lack of a sparkling coloration, *S. babaulti* is maintained by only a few specialists.

In 1989 I had the opportunity to bring back alive a new variant of this species which had not been known before. Males of this variant show yellow instead of beige vertical bars. Moreover there are a number of bright red spots sprinkled over the upper part of the body. The latter feature reminds us of *S. pleurospilus* (see photo) and possibly these two species have a much closer relationship than has been thought previously. Females of this variant, which have a maximum size of approximately 8 cm, have a very attractive colour pattern consisting of a large red blotch covering the head, ventral fins and part of the body. The intensity of the red pigment varies according the emotional state of the fish.

I found this variant in a shallow intermediate habitat a few miles north of Nyanza, Burundi.

A female *Simochromis babaulti* from Nyanza, Burundi.

An adult male *Simochromis pleurospilus* from Zambia.

17

Xenotilapia ornatipinnis Boulenger, 1901

Mark Smith

A courting male *Xenotilapia ornatipinnis*. Photos by Mark Smith.

Xenotilapia ornatipinnis has recently been imported under the name of "Pearly Xenotilapia". The fishes currently in the hobby are collected from the northern part of the lake and were exported by Fishes of Burundi.

X. ornatipinnis is known to occur down to depths of 150 metres (500 feet). However, it also occurs in much shallower waters, a fact which has enabled its collection. As with several species of Tanganyikan cichlids, *X. ornatipinnis* seems to display a wide depth range possibly related to the daily vertical migration of plankton on which it feeds. *X. ornatipinnis* displays a "pearlescent" body coloration so very characteristic of deep living,

A brooding female *Xenotilapia ornatipinnis*.

sand-dwelling cichlids from the lake. Its large, flattened eyes are also marvelous adaptations for living in poorly lit environments. The maximum recorded size is 13 cm (5¼ inches) total length.

In the aquarium, *X. ornatipinnis* readily adapts to the regular aquarium fish food. It behaves very peacefully; never did I observe any torn fins or any individuals cowering in the corners of the aquarium.

X. ornatipinnis has been bred in the aquarium and in most instances the female broods her embryos to full term on her own. Ron Sousy (pers. comm.) found, however, that the female would sometimes give the several days old embryos to the male who would then incubate the developing embryos to full term. On one occasion a carrying male gave the developing embryos to yet another male! This foster father held for a little more than one day before disposing of the brood. To know whether or not this is a naturally occurring event is difficult to ascertain but it seems unlikely that a species which does not seem to form pairs and whose males spawn with several females in a few days, would normally behave in this manner.

X. ornatipinnis is thus a very interesting Tanganyikan cichlid which may provide us with even more surprises. Its refined attractiveness and peaceful behavior should help to establish its popularity among aquarists in the years to come.

Ctenochromis benthicola (Matthes, 1962)

Mark Smith

A female *Ctenochromis benthicola*. This specimen was imported as "Orange Compressiceps". Photographer unknown.

One of the most unusual and rare cichlids presently known from Lake Tanganyika is *Ctenochromis benthicola*. The specimen in the accompanying photograph is a female from the northern end of the lake. This individual somehow made its way into the U.S.A. in the early 70's under the name of "Orange Compressiceps". Whether or not more of these cichlids were ever brought out of the lake for the aquarium hobby is uncertain.

Before Poll's revision of the Tanganyikan cichlids (1986) this species was included in the genus *Haplochromis*. Now it is assigned to *Ctenochromis*, which seems to be an odd genus since representatives of it are found well outside of Lake Tanganyika and seem to be of a different lineage.

Males of this species are a dark brown with a dark blue overlay, while females are entirely orange with just a few black specks on the sides of the body. This peculiar color scheme is unique among Tanganyikan cichlids. The brilliant orange color of the female would seem to make it more conspicuous.

The intense competition in the shallow waters of Lake Tanganyika explain why this fish inhabits only the deeper waters. Its scarcity in the lake may also be due to the greater success of other cichlids causing *C. benthicola*'s numbers to dwindle, indicating that it is on its way to a natural extinction in the years to follow. On the other hand some species naturally have small numbers because that keeps them in balance with *their* biotope.

C. benthicola is also endowed with enlarged sensory pits in the head, a feature shared with members of the genus *Trematocara*, which also inhabit great depths. These enlarged pits probably enable these cichlids to find their food in the relative absence of light.

C. benthicola was successfully bred by the Brichards in the mid 70's. Curiously details of its reproduction were absent from their report, but since only a very few juveniles were produced it may be that *C. benthicola* is a mouthbrooder like all other haplochromines. The juveniles were brown at a length of about 5 cm and thus looked like their father. Some questions must arise from this bit of information. Did the spawn contain only males or do females start out looking like the brown males and then change color as they mature. Another possibility is that the orange females are a kind of color morph, like the O and OB color morphs among Malawian cichlids. (According to Mireille Schreyen from Fishes of Burundi, brown females occur as well making it likely that the orange individuals are indeed a polymorph. *Ed.*).

Neolamprologus petricola (Poll, 1949)

A wild caught male *Neolamprologus petricola*.

The name "Lamprologus Petricola" has been around in the hobby for a long time. It was given to the yellow morphs of *Neolamprologus mustax* and seems still to be in use. Interestingly, *Neolamprologus petricola* resembles *N. moorii* and *N. modestus* more than *N. mustax*. The name *petricola* means "living among rocks" and alludes to the assumption that this cichlid is restricted to rocky habitats. *N. petricola* inhabits the intermediate biotopes along the southwestern coast of the lake. It has never been observed in Zambia. Almost all specimens exported were collected south of Moba in Zaïre, but it is found as far north as Cap Tembwe.

It is very difficult to formulate a distinction between *N. petricola* and *N. modestus*, especially when semi-adult. Both species have an elongated shape, but, in general, *N. modestus* has a shallower body. Both species have a dark brown coloration but under sub-optimal conditions both species show a much lighter pattern. *N. modestus*, in such circumstances, has a much yellower tinge than the beige-greyish colored *N. petricola*. Submissive coloration of the latter species shows grey, broad vertical bars on an almost white background. I have never seen the forms of *N. modestus* from areas other than the deep south of the lake and these types are characterized by bright yellow pectoral fins. The pectorals of *N.* *petricola* are colorless or greyish but never yellow. Large specimens of *N. petricola* show a cranial gibbosity which has never been observed in *N. modestus*. The latter species has thicker lips too, but the teeth on the pharyngeal jaws are similar and indicate a diet of hard invertebrates for both species. The two species may differ in habitat preference as *N. petricola* is also found at deeper levels whereas *N. modestus* seems to be restricted to the shallow regions of the sediment-rich intermediate biotope.

The first observations in the aquarium indicate that *N. petricola* is a territorial cichlid which is difficult to house with conspecifics in a small tank (less than 200 litres). The sexes are easily recognized by examining the vents and thus a single pair can be selected and placed in a large tank. It is the female who starts digging a nest under a rock and she tries to attract the male to her nest.

N. petricola grows to a size of about 13 cm and it seems to attain the deeper body and the gibbosity on the head only at adult size. As in *N. moorii* the female is slightly larger than the male and she is able to produce large spawns. A spawn from a relatively young female numbered more than 300 fry and it seems that fully grown females are able to produce more than 500 eggs per spawn. The juveniles have a light grey color.

Neolamprologus leloupi (Poll, 1956)

Neolamprologus leloupi at Kanoni, Zaïre.

In the first volume of the "Cichlids Yearbook" I have written an entry about a *Neolamprologus* with a yellow dorsal fin which I named *N. leloupi*. At that time I had not observed this species in its natural environment and agreed with Brichard ("Cichlids and all the other fish of Lake Tanganyika", 1990: 537), who had surveyed the entire Zaïrean coast, that *N. caudopunctatus* is a synonym of *N. leloupi*.

In September 1991, Martin Geerts and I made a short visit to the southern Zaïrean part of the lake and also dived near a village named Kapampa. In this area the distributions of *N. leloupi* and of *N. caudopunctatus* overlap. This is also the only location where *N. caudopunctatus* has a bright yellow dorsal. This may have been the sole reason why these two species do not hybridize. *N. leloupi* is distributed north from Kapampa up to Cape Tembwe whereas *N. caudopunctatus* is found south from this region (including the entire Zambian shoreline of the lake).

N. leloupi occurs in several population which differ slightly in the markings in the fins. There is no difference between its behaviour and that of *N. caudopunctatus*, and at Kapampa groups of both species are found side by side in the intermediate habitat. They occur from the shallows to a depth of about 25 m.

Neolamprologus leloupi at Kapampa.

Neolamprologus caudopunctatus at Kapampa.

Neolamprologus sp. "Ubwari Buescheri"

Mark Smith

One of the first exported *Neolamprologus* sp. "Ubwari Buescheri". Photo by Mark Smith.

The existence of this undescribed *Neolamprologus* sp. "Ubwari Buescheri" was first made known photographically to the aquarium world in Axelrod's Aquarium Atlas (1985; first ed. p 511, plate # 349) where it was wrongly identified as *Lamprologus buescheri*. According to Pierre Brichard (1990), his son Thierry discovered this lamprologine at the Ubwari Peninsula in February of 1984. Konings (1988) reports that a specimen of this species was found together with a collection of other cichlids from Burundi, which could indicate that it is also found in this part of the lake. (It has not yet been observed in Burundi waters. See next page for the discussion of a similar species from the Kavala Islands. *Ed*.)

There are a number of differences between this species and *N. buescheri*. The "Ubwari Buescheri" has smaller, more numerous scales than *N. buescheri* from the southern part of the lake. The horizontal striping in *N.* sp. "Ubwari Buescheri" is much narrower —it can at times even fade completely in some aquarium specimens— than that of *N. buescheri*. The basic pattern of *N. buescheri* consists of two horizontal stripes and several vertical stripes. Depending on the location either the vertical striping (Gombi population) or the horizontal striping (Kachese population) is predominant or else a combination of both patterns is present (Chituta Bay population). *N.*

sp. "Ubwari Buescheri" does not show such geographical variation. In fact the upper horizontal stripe of this species is at a noticeably different angle than in *N. buescheri*. Furthermore *N.* sp. "Ubwari Buescheri" shows cranial gibbosity at a small size, 6-7 cm TL, suggesting that 6-7 cm constitutes the adult size for this fish. This cranial gibbosity seems to be lacking in *N. buescheri* for the most part. Lastly, from superficial observations, the trailing ends of the unpaired fins of *N.* sp. "Ubwari Buescheri" tend to be finer or thread-like in contrast to the thicker fin-tips seen in *N. buescheri*. All these observations plus further scientific analysis of this lamprologine will undoubtedly show that these two cichlids are not conspecific.

N. sp. "Ubwari Buescheri" was found at a depth range of 15 to 25 metres, a range that basically matches that of *N. buescheri*. It has also proven itself a territorial aquarium resident; like *N. buescheri* it forms pairs and defends a small section of the aquarium as a territory.

The five specimens, two females and three males, we keep in our tanks have yet to reproduce, but it is probably safe to say that they spawn in the same fashion as similar-sized, rock-dwelling lamprologines do. The finely elongated fins make *N.* sp. "Ubwari Buescheri" a graceful addition to the spectrum of Tanganyikan cichlids.

Neolamprologus sp. "Kavalla"

A male *Neolamprologus* sp. "Kavalla" photographed at Milima Island at a depth of about 15 m.

Neolamprologus sp. "Kavalla" closely resembles *N.* sp. "Ubwari Buescheri" (see previous page) in shape and in some of its pigmentation pattern but grows to a much larger mature size. The maximum size of *N.* sp. "Kavalla" is estimated at 12 cm (no specimens were collected for closer examination).

I have observed this attractive cichlid at Milima Island, one of the islands in the Kavalla archipelago north of Kalemie on the Zaïrean shores of the lake. Its biotope consists of large, rounded boulders which showed at the time of my visit (September 1991) just a thin layer of biocover. The coast around the island shelves gradually to a depth of about 30 m where the habitat becomes predominantly sandy. *N.* sp. "Kavalla" is seen from 10 m on to the edge of the rocky part at about 30 m. It normally occurs solitary and is not common. One would expect that, like *N. buescheri*, males at least would have territories, but territorial individuals were not seen. It seems that *N.* sp. "Kavalla" roams through the biotope in search of food which presumably consists of invertebrates. It was frequently seen swimming in and out of caves in which it may find most of its food. In this respect it behaves more like *N. leleupi* than like *N. buescheri*.

Only the larger individuals, presumably males,

show a grey-blue colour on head and body. Smaller specimens, probably females and sub-adults, rarely display the grey-blue colour. These individuals show a basic pattern of two horizontal lines in which they resemble *N.* sp. "Ubwari Buescheri".

All adult specimens have a dark grey-brown patch on the lower part of the head, which is most intensely coloured near the chin where it abruptly disappears, leaving a pure white chin.

Although the observation that adult size and coloration differ from those of *N.* sp. "Ubwari Buescheri", it is still possible that we are dealing with two populations of one species. Not until the rocky regions between Ubwari and Kavalla have been investigated and no intermediate Lampro-logines have been found may we conclude that these two populations belong to different species.

The basic pigmentation pattern, i.e. the two horizontal lines on the body, is seen in a small number of cichlids belonging to *Neolamprologus* as well as *Lamprologus*. It seems to be a characteristic of cichlids which are rare and usually live at deep levels. Besides the two species mentioned here there is also *L.* sp. "Zambia" (see photo in "Tanganyika Cichlids" by Konings, 1988: 108) and frightened specimens of *N.* sp. "Cygnus" (see photo in "Cichlids Yearbook", vol. 1, 1991: 11) having such a colour pattern.

Cyphotilapia frontosa (Boulenger, 1908)

The race of *Cyphotilapia frontosa* at Kavalla, Zaïre (photo above) resembles that of Burundi.

Plecodus straeleni photographed in Burundi waters.

The first live specimens of *Cyphotilapia frontosa* were exported by Fishes of Burundi in the late fifties. From then on it has been a mainstay in the aquarium hobby and become widespread among aquarists.

C. frontosa has a lake-wide distribution and occurs in several distinguishable races. Initially only the populations of Burundi were exploited. Then the Kigoma race was introduced to the hobby. The latter variant shows one vertical band more on the body than the Burundi race and has thus become known as the Seven-Band Frontosa. In view of the other variants known to date it is better to refer to it as *C. frontosa* (Kigoma).

It is characterized mainly by the dark blue colour on the cheeks and the variable yellow coloration in the dorsal fin. The third variant exported from the lake comes from Zambian waters. It is characterized by a brighter blue coloration (in comparison with the northern races) and an interorbital band. In the late eighties a very dense population of *C. frontosa* was discovered near the Kavalla archipelago in Zaïre. This variant resembles the Burundi race but occurs in rather shallow water (up to 5 metres).

In 1990 Alain Gillot (Zaïre Cichlids) discovered a new and exciting variant of the *frontosa*. This population is characterized by the intense blue colour on all fins and the mother of pearl on the hump and upper part of the body in large specimens. Juveniles also show the attractive blue coloration seen in adults. There is, however, one drawback; it occurs at deep to very deep levels. The shallowest point I have seen this blue *frontosa* was 25 metres. Most specimens are collected at a depth between 40 and 60 metres and require three days to decompress. The blue variant is distributed on the rocky shores between M'Toto and Kapampa on the Zaïrean coast.

An interesting phenomenon is the occurrence of a scale-eating cichlid, *Plecodus straeleni*, which has an identical coloration to that of *C. frontosa*. It was reported (Brichard, 1978, 1989; Krüter, pers.

The blue race of *Cyphotilapia frontosa* is distributed along the southern part of the Zaïrean coast.

comm.) that *P. straeleni* uses its coloration as a camouflage which enables it to mix with groups of *C. frontosa* and stealthily scrape some scales from the flanks of the surprised *frontosas*. I have never observed *P. straeleni* attacking *C. frontosa* although I have seen them among their schools. However, I have observed *P. straeleni* attacking other cichlids, like *Cyathopharynx furcifer* or even the much smaller *Neolamprologus brichardi*.

It has also been said that it may mimic not only *C. frontosa* but also *Neolamprologus sexfasciatus* and *N. tretocephalus*. There are several reasons why this seems unlikely. First of all *P. straeleni* resembles *C. frontosa* to such an extent that it is easily mistaken for its model, even at close quarters. It goes to great lengths to copy *C. frontosa*, so much so that the population at Kapampa has a much bluer coloration (like *C. frontosa*) than that at Rutunga, Burundi (see photographs). Secondly, in Burundi waters there are no *N. sexfasciatus* or *N. tretocephalus*, which would of course not exclude the theory that *P. straeleni*'s colour pattern could have developed in mimicry of those species, but it would make the extreme resemblance to *C. frontosa* at locations where these two species are found inexplicable. Thirdly we could argue that other scale-eaters, especially the abundantly present *Perissodus microlepis*, do not mimic their prey. If we

Plecodus straeleni at Kapampa, Zaïre.

combine this with the observation that *P. straeleni* attacks other cichlids than *C. frontosa* then it seems unlikely that *P. straeleni* needs its coloration to be able to exist predominantly on scales of *C. frontosa*.

C. frontosa roams about in the rocky biotope but it has never been seen hunting prey. Other species inhabiting the same biotope probably know its peaceful manners and thus give *P. straeleni*, dressed in a "sheepskin", a good opportunity. Feigning to be a good-natured *C. frontosa*, the scale-eater comfortably closes in on its prey and before the victim recognizes the wolf it has lost some of its scales.

Cyprichromis sp. "Leptosoma Jumbo"

The yellow morph of *Cyprichromis* sp. "Leptosoma Jumbo" at Kitumba, Zaïre.

The genus *Cyprichromis* consists of several species which belong to the most colourful cichlids of Lake Tanganyika. Representatives of the genus are found at most rocky regions around the lake but none of the species has a lake-wide distribution. Only two species are scientifically described but at least two others are known to occur. At some locations in Zambia (e.g. Mpulungu; René Krüter, pers. comm.) and Tanzania (e.g. Malasa Island; Walter Dieckhoff, pers. comm.) two species of *Cyprichromis* are found sympatrically, but at most other locations it seems that only one species of this genus occurs. However, they are usually found sympatrically with *Paracyprichromis brieni* and *P. nigripinnis*.

It is generally known that in a single population of *Cyprichromis* males with a noticeably different colour pattern, especially in the tail, occur in the same school. I have suggested before (1988) that the blue-tailed individuals could in theory be a genetically different species from the yellow-tailed specimens. Their behavioural preference for feeding from plankton above rocky substrates may have brought these two theoretical species together as it brought *Paracyprichromis*, which has a similar feeding behaviour but is from a different ancestry, together with *Cyprichromis*.

The observation that a female may give birth to yellow as well as blue tailed males in captivity does not prove the natural cause of things. Such a female, e.g. originally a yellow-tailed "species", may have spawned with a blue-tailed male in the confines of an aquarium. If the colour of the tail constitutes the main criterion for mate-recognition, such a female would never have done so in the wild. Until unambiguous experiments have been performed revealing the inheritance of the colour of the tail, the possibility of two sympatric species cannot be excluded.

Sometimes, when such "hybridization" experiments seem to have occurred in the wild, we may deduce false clues regarding the specific status of the different sympatric species. This may be the case with the population of *Cyprichromis* at Kitumba, Zaïre. In this population not only the colour of the tail differs but also the colour on the body. In fact there are three different morphs (or species?): there are completely yellow coloured males and blue coloured males with yellow and blue tails.

I could observe this school for only one hour but during this short period I gained the impression that the complete yellow individuals and the blue individuals represent two different species. As is usual among *Cyprichromis*, males defend their three-dimensional territory in the open water and relate the boundaries to the distance from neighbouring males. Yellow and blue males were

Notice a small aberration in this male's tailfin.

A male of the yellow morph with a broad blue segment.

found mixed and among them large numbers of females, which all looked identical, tried to find a partner to spawn. Both types of males sometimes courted the same female but their territorial aggression was always directed towards a male of the same colour; i.e. yellow males would chase only other yellow males while blue males (with blue or yellow tails) chased only other blue males. Sometimes a chase followed a route through the territory of a differently coloured male!

After a while I noticed a few rare individuals which looked like a cross between the two morphs. Although I do not know what a cross between these two morphs would look like, the colour patterns these individuals showed did not indicate that a cross would yield similar looking offspring. The colour aberration I noticed and photographed (see accompanying pictures) were mainly a type of local mutation rather than a recurrent pattern of a segregation of the parental colors. So there was a mainly yellow individual with a blue blotch on its body or vice versa, a blue male with a yellow spot. Although it cannot be denied that the yellow males are distinctly different from the blue ones, it is still not clear whether females appreciate these differences as well. The fact that I could find three aberrant individuals among a few hundred males may indicate that they are not products of an

The dorsal fin of the male of the blue morph (here with yellow tail) becomes almost white when he courts.

extremely rare event.

These observations can be explained in several different ways of which true hybridization of two sympatric but distinct species is just one. The yellow and blue males could represent different morphs of one species and a female would spawn with all three of them. The territorial colour of the males could be regulated by one or very few genes which could act like a switch in a juvenile phase of the male: normally it would switch on either blue or yellow but in some individuals and at certain regions of the body the switch could have been reversed. This could occur as a phenotypic event, independently from genetic factors.

If the males of this population are to be regarded as morphs of one species then they certainly present a remarkable case of polymorphism (see photographs for how different the two morphs are). If the two morphs represent two species then the definition of a natural species (specific recognition under natural circumstances) seems to be in need of a revision because females apparently can mistake a male of the other species as their true mate. Mary Bailey (pers. comm.), however, suggests that misfertilisation could easily occur in a mêlée, and that the odd males I saw were probably an insignificant part of the total population.

If such contrastingly coloured males can belong to one species then how can we explain the existence of two species of *Cyprichromis* at Malasa Island and Mpulungu? The colour difference between the males of these two species is much less dramatic than in the Kitumba population. Maybe the latter population can teach us a lesson on speciation. It may turn out that coloration is not the most important criterion in species recognition but that species specific odours combined with behavioural and morphological characters play a major role instead.

A possible advantage for *Cyprichromis* having differently coloured males which do not visually recognize each other as belonging to the same species, is that their territories can be closer together without eliciting constant territorial fights of similar looking, neighbouring males. Indeed I frequently observed yellow and blue territorial males almost perfectly alternating in the water column.

For the time being I regard the Kitumba population as belonging to one, polymorphic species, namely *Cyprichromis* sp. "Leptosoma Jumbo".

The completely blue morph of *Cyprichromis* sp. "Leptosoma Jumbo" from Kitumba.

Paracyprichromis brieni (Poll, 1948)

A wildcaught male *Paracyprichromis brieni* collected at Kitumba, Zaïre. Note the spots in the trailing part of the dorsal fin.

A female *Paracyprichromis brieni* (Velifer).

When the first specimens of this pretty little cichlid —with the trade name "Cyprichromis Velifer"— arrived in western aquarists' tanks it was immediately thought that the individuals with the attractive black and white dorsal fins were males and the ones with the plain fins were females.

Of course, after acclimatization and with observations made under less stressful conditions it became apparent that it is the female which is adorned with the black and white dorsal fin.

Due to the lack of yellow coloration on the tips of the ventral fins this species is placed in the genus *Paracyprichromis* rather than *Cyprichromis*.

It is a geographical variant of *P. brieni* which is distributed along the Zaïrean coast between Kitumba and Moba. It has a rather wide depth-range since individuals were observed between 5 and 35 metres.

Since its introduction it has been bred in captivity, but reports concerning a spawning are not yet available. Courting behavior differs slightly in some points from that of *P. nigripinnis*. Males occupy territories, like *P. nigripinnis* males, but these are not necessarily alongside the vertical face of a rock or at the side of the tank. Females stay in the open water as well and form schools. Male *P. nigripinnis* court females by displaying themselves with all fins erect, followed by leading the female to the centre of its territory while swimming in an undulating fashion.

The courting behavior of *P. brieni* (Velifer) differs in that some males do not lead the females while vigourously quivering their bodies. The male starts courting with a display of all its fins accompanied by a slight quivering and sometimes sideways jerking of the body. Meanwhile he inches his way towards the female and, at close range, gives her a sudden blow with his tail.

Males *P. brieni* (Velifer) are characterized by a black spot in the middle of the tailfin. As far as is known this is the only geographical variant of *P. brieni* with such a feature.

MALAŴIAN CICHLIDS

The genus *Cynotilapia* Regan 1922

Dr. Andreas Spreinat

The main typical feature of the species of the genus *Cynotilapia is* unicuspid teeth, spaced relatively far apart and resembling the teeth of a predator. Most other morphological characteristics resemble those of the members of the *Pseudotropheus zebra* complex to such an extent that without knowledge of the tooth structure, they can easily be confused with these mbuna. In nature another feature can be observed that further differentiates *Cynotilapia* from *Pseudotropheus*: in contrast to most other mbuna, *Cynotilapia*, except for territorial males, forages in the water column several feet above the rocky

substrate. Their food consists of plankton rather than of *Aufwuchs*. The unicuspid, widely spaced, teeth are better suited to the capture of small planktonic invertebrates (zooplankton) than to combing the algae of the biocover.

The type species, *C. afra*, was described in 1893 by the ichthyologist Albert Günther, who worked at the British Museum (Natural History). In 1976, the second species in this genus, *C. axelrodi*, was described by Burgess. Tony Ribbink and his co-workers, a South African team of ichthyologists, concluded, after the investigation of many rocky habitats along the shores of Lake Malaŵi, that a

A male *Cynotilapia afra* in the rocky habitat around Chitandi Island; note its teeth!. Photo by A. Spreinat.

further 8 species of *Cynotilapia* exist (Ribbink *et al.*, 1983). These species were not formally described but given provisional names.

Probably even more species exist. Some time ago specimens from a population of *Cynotilapia* were imported under the trade name "Jaro Afra". These cichlids, collected at Jalo Reef near Nkhota Kota, belong to a scientifically undescribed species provisionally called *C.* sp. "Jalo".

Among aquarists *C. afra* is the best known species. I am not aware when it was exported for the first time, but it must have been in the late sixties or early seventies. *C. afra* is found in the northern half of the lake. Likoma, Chizumulu and the rocky shores between Chirombo Point and Ngara on the West coast are known to harbour this mbuna.

The variation in the colour pattern of *C. afra* is noteworthy. On the one hand populations show geographical variation in male breeding coloration, and on the other hand variations exist within a single population. These variations are not just subtle changes in the colour pattern but include conspicuous differences in the nuptial coloration of males, especially the coloration of the dorsal fin. Ribbink and his coworkers investigated the differences in the coloration of the dorsal fins of males in the populations inhabiting the northern shores of Likoma Island.

They found that the number of males with black dorsal fins decreased towards the south, whereas males with white or yellow dorsal fins became more abundant there.

Among aquarists it was previously common practice to differentiate between *Cynotilapia* and *Pseudotropheus* by looking at the vertical bars on the body. These continued into the dorsal fin in *Cynotilapia* and not in *Pseudotropheus*. Owing to the increased knowledge of species and geographical variants this criterion has been invalidated, as some species of *Cynotilapia* are known to have entirely white dorsal fins while some members of the *Pseudotropheus zebra* complex have vertical barring extending into this fin.

Given the considerable variation known to occur within a population of *C. afra*, it is difficult to assess whether in other populations we are dealing with a geographical variant or with a different species. Complicated and elaborate investigations are necessary in order to make a final pronouncement.

By comparison the recognition of *C.* sp. "Mbamba" as a valid species is relatively simple. *C.* sp. "Mbamba" lives sympatrically with *C. afra* at most locations albeit at a generally deeper level. Also *C.* sp. "Mbamba" shows a considerable variation in male breeding coloration, geographically as well as within a single

A male with a black dorsal. Is this a geographical variant of *Cynotilapia afra* or a different species? Photos by A. Spreinat.

population. Some individuals are almost completely black, i.e. the black bars are so broad that they cover most of the flanks. Other specimens, however, have a colour pattern not unlike that of *Pseudotropheus zebra*. Some males have a yellow, and others a light blue, blaze on top of the head. This part of the head is also the simplest feature by which one can discrim-inate between *C. afra* and *C.* sp. "Mbamba". *C. afra* has a black interorbital bar (from eye to eye) and a bar across the upper part of the head. This second bar, which runs between the upper parts of the gillcovers, is lacking in *C.* sp. "Mbamba". Sometimes a faint trace of the bar is visible but the background colour, yellow or light blue, is clearly visible giving the fish the appearance of having a coloured cap.

Unfortunately *C.* sp. "Mbamba" was exported only sporadically although it would make a very attractive addition to the mainstays of the hobby. *C. axelrodi*, however, is a frequently exported member of the genus. It is usually exported under the trade name "Kingsizei". The first specimens were exported by Peter Davies in 1973. For a long time the identity of *C. axelrodi* was uncertain, probably because Burgess, who described the species in 1976, gave as type locality the southern part of the lake (Burgess, 1976: 41). This was the location from which the exporter operated but not where this species was subsequently found. Ribbink and his coworkers (1983) and several diving aquarists found *C. axelrodi* to be restricted to the western coast between Chirombo Point and Lion's Cove. Another species, which belongs to *Pseudotropheus* because of its bicuspid teeth, collected at Likoma Island and also named "Kingsizei", further confused the identity of *C. axelrodi*.

Not only does *C. axelrodi* differ from the other species of the genus in its almost nondescript, light blue coloration, but it also has an elongated shape. The population which I was able to observe north of Nkhata Bay inhabited shallow water over a mixed bottom at a depth of 4-6 metres. Males behaved territorially and defended areas with a diameter of about one meter.

The only other *Cynotilapia* which is elongated like *C. axelrodi*, is the scientifically undescribed *C.* sp. "Lion". This cichlid, with its trade name "Lions Cove Afra", is, as its name indicates, collected near Lion's Cove on the northwestern shore. *C.* sp. "Lion" also prefers a mixed sandy-rocky bottom in shallow water. It is rarely found in waters deeper than 20 metres. Males excavate small caves into which females are led in order to spawn. Like many other mbuna, *C.* sp. "Lion" tends to lose its elongated body-shape when fed copiously. Such specimens are often as deep-

A male *Cynotilapia* sp. "Mbamba" at Chitande Island.

bodied as wild *C. afra*.

The distribution of *C.* sp. "Chinyankwazi" is limited to the two small islets, Chinyankwazi and Chinyamwezi, in the southeastern arm of the lake. (Recently a population has been discovered at Chinyamwezi Reef, *Ed.*). These two islets belong to the National Park and are forbidden grounds for the collection of ornamental fish. The coloration of *C.* sp. "Chinyankwazi" is almost identical to that of *Pseudotropheus zebra*. Interestingly, *P. zebra* is not present at these two islets. It would be worth the effort to investigate how the niche of *C.* sp. "Chinyankwazi" compares with that of *P. zebra*.

It is possible that *C.* sp. "Chinyankwazi" has been exported in earlier times, when collection at these two islands was still allowed. Maybe some specimens of this mbuna are still around in the hobby, possibly under the name *P. zebra* or as an unidentified species.

The other species, for which there is no space for photographs, will be discussed for completeness. Ribbink and his coworkers identified a rare species at Ndumbi Rocks, Likoma Island with the name *C.* sp. "Ndumbi". It lives in secluded caves in shallow water. Its coloration is almost entirely black.

C. sp. "Maleri" is known only from the Maleri Islands (Ribbink *et al.*, 1983). It has a dark blue body with black vertical bars. The Mbenji Islands harbour two species of this genus, *C.* sp. "Yellow Dorsal" and *C.* sp. "Black Dorsal". The main characteristics of the male breeding coloration are used in their unofficial names. *C.* sp. "Jalo" was mentioned earlier in this article.

The maintenance of *Cynotilapia* is not much different from that of other mbuna. Besides a slightly alkaline pH-value of the water and a modest feeding regime, the size of the tank and its decoration is an important factor. Under the right conditions and with a restricted but varied diet *Cynotilapia* behaves as a lively and robust mbuna. As with many other mbuna, territorial *Cynotilapia* can be aggressive towards conspecifics as well as other species.

Most of the imported species can be bred in captivity. However, little has been reported about the inheritance of the different colour patterns in *C. afra* and *C.* sp. "Mbamba", the two species with the variable coloration. There is thus an opportunity, especially for aquarists, to discover some interesting facts about these fascinating mbuna.

References

BURGESS, W.E. (1976) Studies on the family Cichlidae: 7. *Cynotilapia axelrodi*, a new species of Mbuna from Lake Malawi (Pisces: Cichlidae). *Trop. Fish Hobbyist* 24, Oct. pp 37-44.

GÜNTHER, A. (1893) Second report on the reptiles, batrachians and fishes transmitted by Mr. H. H. Johnson, C. B., from British Central Africa. *Proc. zool. Soc. Lond.* pp 616-628.

RIBBINK, A.J., MARSH, B.A., MARSH, A.C., RIBBINK, A.C., and SHARP, B.J. (1983) A preliminary survey of the cichlid fishes of rocky habitats in Lake Malawi. *S. Afr. J. Zool.* 18 (3), pp 149-310.

C. axelrodi 2 km north of Nkhata Bay. Photos by A. Spreinat.

A male *Cynotilapia* sp. "Lion" at Lions Cove.

Cynotilapia sp. "Chinyankwazi" at Chinyankwazi Island.

The *Protomelas taeniolatus*-complex

The race of *Protomelas taeniolatus* at Chinyankwazi Island is better known as "Haplochromis Fire Blue".

Protomelas taeniolatus is one of the most frequently exported non-mbuna from Lake Malawi. In the aquaristic trade it is better known as Haplochromis Steveni. During the lake's evolution many geographical races have developed. Several localities are regularly fished for these variants which have all been given separate names. A few aquarium favourites received names like "Steveni Tiger", "Red Empress", or "Fire Blue", while others were named for the locality where they were collected, e.g. "Steveni Mbenji" or "Steveni Maleri".

It was known to the fish-collectors that one location could harbour two varieties of "Steveni". "Steveni Tiger" and "Steveni Thick Bars" were both caught at Likoma and Chizumulu Island. Although they have different preferences concerning their habitat, both Stevenis could be seen together at some locations. "Steveni Tiger", now identified as *Protomelas taeniolatus*, has thin vertical bars on a silvery body, whereas "Steveni Thick Bars" has broad vertical bars. The nuptial coloration of the male differs too. A "Steveni Tiger" male has an intense blue on the head and upper part of the body and an intense orange-yellow on the flanks. A "Steveni Thick Bars" male has a light blue breeding coloration and a yellow throat. Its colours are much less intense compared to the "Steveni Tiger".

From the previous description it must be clear that we are dealing with two different species which can be found sympatrically. Ten years ago the scientific identification of these two species was still unclear. It was Tony Ribbink and his coworkers (1983) who gave us important new information about these two species. They pointed to the fact that these two species behave differently. *Protomelas taeniolatus*, the most common of the two, feeds on the biocover in the upper regions of the rocky habitat. Its food consists mainly of algae. *Protomelas fenestratus*, the "Steveni Thick Bars", lives in the deeper regions of the rocky biotope and blows away the sediment on the rocks to reveal its prey, which consists mostly of insect larvae and crustaceans.

Even though in shape and appearance these two species are sometimes difficult to distinguish, by observing their feeding behaviour one can easily identify them. Ribbink et al. (1983) further noted that the colour pattern of *P. fenestratus* consists of conspicuous vertical bars whereas that of *P. taeniolatus* has more horizontal elements. Now, with knowledge of behaviour and coloration it must be easy to identify all populations of these cichlids in the lake. Initially, it seemed to work. I could (I thought) identify every population even though I found that the pattern of markings, especially in *P. taeniolatus*, varied considerably (which was also mentioned by Ribbink *et al.*). After more than 250 hours of diving experience in the lake, the identification of these species looks less simple. *P. taeniolatus* is very common and territorial males are found on almost every rocky shore. *P. fenestratus* is much rarer but can be found at most rocky areas as well. Breeding males are not common. They are weakly territorial and usually construct a shallow nest in the sand alongside a rock. At Hora Mhango, on the northwestern coast of the lake, *P. fenestratus* was found to defend a territory on top of a rock, like *P. taeniolatus* does. I also found two other species which blow in the substrate as part of their feeding behavior. One of these, *P. pleurotaenia*, lives in the shallow sandy and vegetated areas and does not show geographical variation. Its pattern consists of two thin, horizontal lines on a silvery body. The other species is closely related to *Placidochromis johnstoni* and therefore easily distinguished from *P. fenestratus*. As far as I know, a cichlid with a small mouth, vertical barring, and blowing in the sediment is a sure identification for *P. fenestratus*. In May 1989 I found at Kande Island (and at Mphandikucha Island) a Steveni-type cichlid which had the lower half of the body completely

black. I photographed another Steveni-type as well but could not collect it. Since the latter specimen showed distinct vertical bars I provisionally identified it as *P. fenestratus* although I didn't see it blowing in the sand. I examined one specimen of the black-bellied Steveni and could not find any distinction between it and *P. taeniolatus*. I Therefore thought it to be a geographical race of the latter species. In November 1990 I re-visited the northwestern coast and found black-bellied Stevenis at most locations, albeit in very low numbers. Furthermore I found a (blowing) *P. fenestratus* at Kande Island which had a heavily barred colour pattern, unlike the one I had seen before. My conclusion is that there are at least three species in the *P. taeniolatus* complex. All of these species can be found sympatrically. The black-bellied Steveni is common only at Kande and Mphandikucha Islands. Its coloration seems to be quite constant along the northwestern shores. Territorial males defend a nest on a rock or on the sand beside a rock. The rocky areas around the Nsinje river delta on the east coast of Lake Malaŵi provided me with another problem. In this area the so-called "Steveni Eastern" is collected. At first, I had

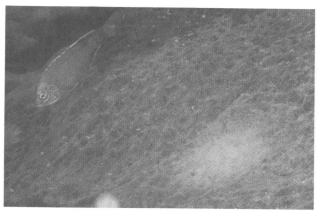

The algal-garden denotes the centre of the territory of this male *P. taeniolatus* (Thumbi West Island).

The "Steveni Eastern" is a race of *Protomels taeniolatus*.

A male *Protomelas* sp. "Steveni Blue Black" (Masinje).

A *Protomelas* sp. "Steveni Black-Belly" at Mdoka.

identified this cichlid as *P. taeniolatus* (Konings, 1989). During a later visit I found, north of the river, another Steveni-type. The males were completely blue (see photo) and stayed in the upper regions of the habitat. At the same time, at deeper levels, I observed *P. fenestratus* females blowing away in the sand. I then concluded that the "Steveni Eastern" must be *P. fenestratus*, as I found males at deeper levels than the all-blue Steveni. Moreover I saw a male "Steveni Eastern" displaying for such a sand-blowing female. My only reservation at that time was that the females, which were normally shipped with "Steveni Eastern", didn't show much vertical barring whereas the sediment-blowing females had distinct vertical bars. I never questioned the fishermen about this matter, which I should have done. In a later publication (1990) I showed the "Steveni Eastern" as *P. fenestratus*.

During my third visit to the area I found territorial males of *P. fenestratus* which looked like anything but "Steveni Eastern". The coloration of these males is very much like that of "Steveni Thick Bars" at Likoma and Chizumulu Islands. So there are three species at the eastern shores as well. "Steveni Eastern" is a race of *P. taeniolatus* in which the females have few markings on a silvery body. The *P. fenestratus* has never been exported and thus lacks a trade name.

The third species, in which the males are blue, could in fact be closely related to the black-bellied Steveni from the northwestern shores. I have not seen females which could confirm this idea, but the shape of the short snout resembles that of the northern species. For the time being, however, we will refer to the blue Steveni as *Protomelas* sp. "Steveni Blue Black".

A reef north of Chizumulu Island, named Taiwan Reef, harbours only one member of the *P. taeniolatus* complex. The reef consists of large rocks which meet the sandy bottom at great depths. The depth and strong current, which is commonly observed around the reef, make the

A female with an unusual colour pattern but identified as *P. fenestratus* because of her particular feeding technique.

A male *Protomelas fenestratus* at its shallow nest in the sand (Nsinje River Outlet).

rocks virtually devoid of sediment. The Steveni at Taiwan has very broad, vertical bars but I have not seen them blowing into the biocover. If it were *P. fenestratus* this could be explained by there being no sediment to blow in (*P. fenestratus* hardly ever blows in the gravel in an aquarium). After examining several specimens I must conclude that the "Steveni Taiwan" is not a race of *P. fenestratus*. Its anatomy is closer to that of *P. taeniolatus* but I now think it is better to regard it as a different species altogether. I don't like to split up species-complexes into many different species, because, although it seems to solve a taxonomic problem, it is like turning your back on the really interesting questions like variation, speciation, and evolution.

Taiwan Reef may be the only isolated place in the lake that has harboured a viable population of cichlids, even during the low water stands. We may thus expect to find old species at this reef. Species that were probably never in direct contact with their sibling species elsewhere in the lake. Speciation may therefore have come to a stasis long ago. There are not many purely rock-dwelling cichlids at the reef; there is only one species of the *Pseudotropheus zebra*-complex, one from the *Ps. tropheops*-complex, two from the *Ps. elongatus*-complex; there is only one *Melanochromis* and there are no species from the genus

Labidochromis. *Protomelas* sp. "Steveni Taiwan" behaves as *P. taeniolatus* but males defend their nests at depths below 20 metres. *P. taeniolatus* lives mostly in the upper 10 metres at any rocky coast I have visited. Most of the year there is a heavy current around Taiwan Reef, sometimes so strong that it is difficult to swim against, even with fins! The only species that braves such a current is *Pseudotropheus saulosi*. *P.* sp. "Steveni Taiwan" may have been forced by the current to dwell in deeper regions. *P. taeniolatus* and the "Steveni Taiwan" may have the same ancestor but due to the complete isolation from all other populations it has developed into a different species, adapted to its specific environment. Its relatively large eye could therefore be an adaptation to the depth at which it lives.

References

KONINGS, A. (1989) *Malaŵi cichlids in their natural habitat.* Verduijn Cichlids, Zevenhuizen, Netherlands
KONINGS, A. (1990) *Book of cichlids and all the other fishes of Lake Malaŵi.* TFH Publications, Neptune, USA.
RIBBINK, A.J., MARSH, B.A., MARSH, A.C., RIBBINK, A.C., & SHARP, B.J. (1983) A preliminary survey of the cichlid fishes of rocky habitats in Lake Malaŵi. *S.-Afr. J. Zool.* Vol. 18, (3).

Protomelas sp. "Steveni Taiwan" is easily the most beautiful species of the *P. taeniolatus*-complex.

Tramitichromis lituris (Trewavas, 1931)

A territorial male *Tramitichromis lituris* (Mdoka).

The genus *Tramitichromis* is characterised by the peculiar shape of the lower pharyngeal bone. The teeth on this bone are all slender and long. The teeth situated at the front are the longest, which is an unusual feature. These long anterior teeth are further characterised by their long tips which are bent backwards. In most other species the anterior teeth are small and their tips point forward. The reason for this particular development in *Tramitichromis* is not clear, but most likely its origin lies in the feeding behaviour or in the type of food. Another feature of *Tramitichromis* is the downward projecting blade of the lower pharyngeal bone. The upper edge of this blade runs horizontally in most cichlids but in *Tramitichromis* it projects downwards (more than 50° in *T. variabilis*).

The lower gill-rakers in *Tramitichromis* are short and robust, as in other sand-sifting *Lethrinops*, e.g. *L. leptodon, L. macrochir*. The first two rakers are usually no more than small knobs on the gill-arch. The central three to five rakers on the lower arches are wide and much larger. The tips of the broad rakers together form an almost horizontal platform at the bottom of the buccal cavity. The kind of grid they form may separate the heavier material from the lighter when a mouthful of sand and sediment is taken into the mouth. The heavier sand may thus sink between the rakers and be carried to the outside while the lighter material, including invertebrates and algae, remains inside the mouth. The strength of the rakers is probably needed to withstand the abrasive action of the sand. If the rakers were higher, the separating effect might be more effective. The need to keep the tips of the pharyngeal teeth in the same plane as those of the gill-rakers could have led to the situation in *Tramitichromis* where the anterior teeth are relatively longer than in other cichlids. The anterior pharyngeal teeth of e.g. *Lethrinops leptodon* are not long and are below the level of the raker-tips.

I recognize five, possibly six species, in *Tramitichromis*. Four species are described: *T. brevis, T. variabilis, T. lituris*, and *T. trilineatus*. Because of its different colour pattern I regard *intermedius* — placed in *Tramitichromis* by Eccles & Trewavas (1989) — as a member of the genus *Trematocranus*.

I have never been able to examine specimens of *T. trilineatus*, so all information given here relates to the first three species. *T. brevis* was exported as "Lethrinops Variabilis" or as "Lethrinops Chizumulu" and is easily recognized by its small adult size (about 14 cm) and by the prominent diagonal stripe on its flank.

The type material of *T. variabilis* consists, in my

A female *Tramitichromis lituris* (Mdoka).

A male *T. brevis* at its cave-crater nest. (Chizumulu)

A cave-crater nest of *Tramitichromis lituris*.

A *Tramitichromis lituris* nest on top of a rock.

"Lethrinops Red Flush", possibly *Tramitichromis variabilis*, is collected in Senga Bay.

The lower pharyngeal jaw of *Tramitichromis lituris*.

A *T. variabilis*-type lower pharyngeal bone; note the steeply inclined anterior blade. Photos by Gertrud Dudin.

opinion, of at least two different species. Specimens of one of these are exported as "Lethrinops Red Flush" and they were all collected in Senga Bay. This species has only vague markings on the body. Trewavas (1931) reports that the northern races (species?) have (mostly) a diagonal stripe. Such specimens have been collected around Likoma and Chizumulu Island.

T. lituris has recently been observed in its natural biotope but has never, to my knowledge, been exported. A species which I previously identified as *T. lituris*, is probably an undescribed, but closely related species (Konings, 1990). They came from Senga Bay but have, since their first importation, never been seen again.

I have reported on the breeding behaviour of *T. brevis* (Konings, 1990) and can add only that breeding was also observed in November. Since Stuart Grant collected males in breeding colour in April, it may be possible that *T. brevis* breeds throughout the year. The main feature of the male's nest is a small stone under (and around) which a semi-circular rim of sand (oxbow) is deposited (see photo), the so-called cave-crater nest. The female lays her eggs as far as possible under the small stone.

A breeding colony of *T. lituris* was observed near Mdoka at the end of November. Most members of the school were found between a depth of 7 to 15 metres. Territorial males had constructed a cave-crater nest. Similar nests are constructed by *T. brevis* although they use smaller stones. The breeding colony of *T. lituris* was mixed with a breeding colony of *Nyassachromis eucinostomus* the males of which build shallow nests in the sand when at deeper (than 7 m) levels. It is known with regard to *N. eucinostomus* that some males construct a sand-nest on top of rocks whenever there is a lack of sites on the bottom. The colony at Mdoka had some males defending their nest on top of a rock. Not only *N. eucinostomus* but also *T. lituris* males had made their nests on top of rocks! Such unusual behaviour in utaka can be explained by the observation that its females feed on plankton in the open water and the males are thus closer to the females (even if they have to carry the sand up the rock). *Lethrinops* forages in the sand and males building a nest on top of rocks would diminish their chances of mating. At Mdoka, however, I found females several feet above the substrate and at first I presumed that these were attracted by the males that had their territories on the rocks. When I examined a few preserved specimens I found their long guts (2.5 times standard length) completely filled with phyto-plankton. Hence it is possible that the territorial males have adapted themselves to the situation where females feed in the open water column due to a plankton-bloom.

It is still remarkable that a bottom-feeding species, which apparently needs the protection (during spawning) of a cave-crater nest, switches to an open nest-type a few metres above the floor. I have observed females accepting the alternative nest and spawning with the occupant.

It is not likely that *T. lituris* breeds throughout the year as this species was not seen (at the same location) in May, 1989.

References

ECCLES, D.H. & TREWAVAS, E. (1989) *Malawian cichlid fishes. The classification of some Haplochromine genera.* Lake Fish Movies, Herten, Germany.
KONINGS, A. (1990) *Book of cichlids and all the other fishes of Lake Malawi.* TFH Publications, Neptune, New Jersey.
TREWAVAS, E. (1931) A revision of the cichlid fishes of the genus *Lethrinops*, Regan. *Ann. Mag. nat. Hist.* (10), 7; pp. 133-153.

Stigmatochromis sp. "Modestus Makokola"

A wildcaught male *Stigmatochromis* sp. "Modestus Makokola".

Stigmatochromis sp. "Modestus Makokola" has been exported recently, albeit in low numbers. As its name implies, it is collected at the Makokola Reef, south of Boadzulu Island in the southeastern arm of the lake. It has also been observed at Boadzulu Island.

S. sp. "Modestus Makokola" differs from *S. modestus* in several anatomical features. Its average adult size ranges between 16 and 20 cm. Although *S. modestus* can grow to a size of about 25 cm, most adult specimens have a length between 14 and 18 cm. The "Modestus Makokola" has a deeper body and the three spots are more distinct than in *S. modestus*. The usually dark brown body coloration of *S. modestus* obscures its markings but when stressed, three small, round spots are visible. The first spot (suprapectoral) in *S.* sp. "Modestus Makokola" is elongated and about twice as long as in *S. modestus*. The body coloration of the "Modestus Makakola" is silvery rather than brown.

The teeth of *S.* sp. "Modestus Makokola" are unicuspid and not densely packed, which places it in *Stigmatochromis* rather than *Otopharynx*. I did not observe *S. modestus* at Makokola Reef or at Boadzulu Island, but they were present at Chinyamwezi and Chinyankwazi Islands. Although they were not found together, I believe that the "Modestus Makokola" is a different species and not a geographical variant of *S. modestus*.

There is also a difference in behaviour. *S. modestus* lives in the rocky habitat where it usually hides in the dark recesses. The dark brown coloration blends well with the environment and provides a splendid camouflage. It is a typical ambush hunter, its prey being mainly small mbuna. Only during the breeding period do males stake out a territory in the rocky biotope, often under an overhanging rocky ledge. Territorial males gather in small colonies numbering between 5 and 15 individuals.

The few encounters I had with *S.* sp. "Modestus Makokola" revealed a different behaviour in this predator. During all encounters (only males were observed) the fish was out in the open, not hiding among the rocks. At Makokola Reef it seemed to be more common near the intermediate habitat at a depth of about 35 meters. A few times it was seen cruising over the sand, probably hunting for small, sand-dwelling cichlids which are abundant in that area. At Boadzulu Island it was seen once. There it was seen hunting over large rocks, behaving a little like a pursuit hunter.

Because of its carnivorous appetite it is desirable to accompany *S.* sp. "Modestus Makokola" with larger cichlids. Apart from that it is fairly easy to maintain in a community aquarium.

Dimidiochromis strigatus (Regan, 1922)

Peter Baasch

A territorial male *Dimidiochromis strigatus* photographed in the author's aquarium.

Dimidiochromis strigatus has a lake-wide distribution but it is infrequently collected. Observations in their natural habitat are rare and are restricted to sub-adult individuals with a length of about 12 cm.

Reports about its feeding behaviour range from pursuit piscivore, or feeding on invertebrates, to vegetarian feeding on aquatic plants. If one considers the habitat in which *D. strigatus* is usually found, i.e. the shallow sandy areas, most of the alleged diets could indeed make up *D. strigatus*' dinner. The oblique mouth indicates that insects that have been fallen into the water may also form a part of its diet. The size of its mouth and the observations in the aquarium, however, suggest that it behaves like a ambush predator preferring live food above plants.

D. strigatus is irregularly exported as "Haplochromis Sunset". Most exported specimens have a length of about 12 to 15 cm. The largest specimen ever caught measured 24.4 cm total length.

D. strigatus is laterally compressed, has a rather deep body, and its lower jaw is longer than the upper. The horizontal mid-lateral stripe on the body is a characteristic of all species of *Dimidiochromis*.

Its morphological features resemble those of *D. compressiceps* although its body is deeper and less compressed than that of *D. compressiceps*, which gives it a stouter appearance.

Wild caught male *D. strigatus* start colouring up at a size between 15 and 20 cm. They develop into beautifully coloured cichlids with a charac-teristic red spot behind the gill cover and a red anal fin.

Males defend territories when they have assumed the breeding coloration, and behave rather aggressively towards other inhabitants of the aquarium. Therefore the tank should have a size of at least 150 cm, but 200 cm would be better. In the territory the male constructs a shallow crater with a diameter of about 50 cm and a depth of about 5 to 10 cm.

Spawning takes place in this crater-nest. The number of eggs laid is remarkable. Once one of my females released 230 fry after the incubation period! Raising the fry poses some problems. Besides nitrate-free water, the fry also need close attention when feeding. They don't know when to stop eating. Many casualties may arise when too much food is given at one time. At a size of about 2.5 cm they seem to cope better with the food.

D. strigatus and *D. compressiceps* should be kept separated as hybridization between these two species has frequently been reported. Juveniles of the two species are difficult to tell apart.

Copadichromis boadzulu (Iles, 1960)

Peter Baasch

A courting male *Copadichromis boadzulu*; the female is partly visible in the background.

When one looks through the aquaristic publications for mention of *Haplochromis* or *Cyrtocara boadzulu* one gets the impression that this species is one of the best known of the Malaŵian cichlids. The photographs accompanying articles, however, show a different species to the one on this page. The reason is simple. Those who have read the latest revision of Malaŵi cichlids (Eccles & Trewavas, 1989) and the latest aquaristic literature (Konings, 1989, 1990) know that the cichlid which has been sold for years under names like "Boadzulu", "Hinderi", "Red Empress" or (better!) as "Namalenje" belongs to a geographical race of *Protomelas taeniolatus*. This has left us with the question of what does *C. boadzulu* look like.

The "real" *C. boadzulu* is, as far as I know, a rare cichlid, small populations of which inhabit the sandy regions in the southeastern arm of the lake. Until now only two localities are known, one at Crocodile Rock in 5 metre deep water and one at Makanjila Point where the sand is at a depth of about 15 metres.

Sightings in the natural habitat are very rare; breeding individuals were not seen.

C. boadzulu belongs to the utaka group and feeds predominantly on plankton in the open water. In captivity it eats all kinds of aquarium foods. Although intraspecific aggression remains within tolerable limits, this active cichlid —maximum size is about 14 cm— needs a rather large aquarium. Initially it may be a little panicky and thus care must be taken to cover the tank properly.

The basic pigmentation pattern shows some vertical barring but this is seen mainly in breeding males. The main characteristic is a horizontal mid-lateral line which runs from the third vertical bar to the caudal peduncle. A second horizontal (dorso-lateral) stripe, which is characteristic of *Protomelas taeniolatus*, is entirely absent. Fully coloured males have a white-blue blaze on the head which continues as a white marginal band in the dorsal fin.

Of great interest was the breeding behaviour displayed by a male in my tank. He constructed a turret of sand with a height of about 25 cm! When placed in another aquarium the male again made a sand-cone.

Spawning has not yet been observed. The number of fry released per spawn, however, is rather small and never consisted of more than 19 babies. The basic pigmentation pattern and the construction of a spawning-cone may indicate that *C. boadzulu* belongs to *Nyassachromis*, since most other utaka in *Copadichromis* have a pattern of spots and are not known to build spawning-cones on the sand.

Buccochromis rhoadesii (Boulenger, 1908)

Dr. Andreas Spreinat

A male *Buccochromis rhoadesii* courting a female (in the background). Photo by A. Spreinat.

Only two of the seven species which are currently assigned to the genus *Buccochromis* have experienced a wide distribution among aquarists. *B. lepturus* was imported several years ago under the tradename "Green Lepturus". A second species was first imported under the trade name "Haplochromis Lepturus" and later as "Yellow Lepturus". Its scientific name was uncertain for a long time until the revision of the Malaŵian haplochromines (non-mbuna) by Eccles and Trewavas (1989) was published. Then it became clear that "Yellow Lepturus" had been described under the name *B. rhoadesii*.

B. rhoadesii probably has a lake-wide distribution as it has been caught at several localities around the lake. Most of the exported specimens were collected at Likoma Island. Here young solitary individuals or small groups are regularly seen over mixed sand-rock habitats but also in rocky areas. They are seen in shallow water as well as at depths of 15 to 20 metres.

Our *B. rhoadesii*, which we obtained at a size of approximately 6 to 7 cm, were placed, following a short acclimatization period, in a large tank (250 x 70 cm) together with some other haplochromines. First we noticed that these juveniles showed a voracious appetite. After a year of maintenance the fish had reached a size of about 16 cm but did not show any sign of the sexual dimorphism known from adults. At this stage they all had a yellow coloration which was most intense on the ventral part of the body. At an age of almost two years and at a length of about 18 cm the largest specimens began to show signs of the male adult coloration. The first sign was a blue sheen on the skin between the eyes and mouth which progressed, with age, to the anterior part of the head and, later on, over the entire body. The yellow coloration decreased concomitantly with the appearance of the blue. When I could differentiate between the sexes, I took a pair and placed them in a 3-metre aquarium, while I left the other pair in the tank they grew up in.

The complete metamorphosis of the males took several months. The male in the photograph measures 27 cm while the females, of the same age, measure between 20 and 23 cm.

Notwithstanding its size and robust appearance, *B. rhoadesii* behaves relatively peacefully. Although the males need an area of the aquarium in which they are usually found, they do not systematically defend this as a territory. Females are courted but left unharmed; even during spawning other species are tolerated in the tank. One thing didn't change: their voracious appetite; thus we expect further growth of our fish.

Corematodus taeniatus Trewavas, 1935

Dr. Andreas Spreinat

A territorial male *Corematodus taeniatus* photographed near Fort Maguire. Photo by A. Spreinat.

The first *Corematodus taeniatus* were exported by Norman Edwards under the trade name "Haplochromis Jacksoni". In 1988 Stuart Grant exported this cichlid, which was collected at Namalenje Island, as "Haplochromis Space Mouth". In November that year I received a call from an importer in Bayern that several of these cichlids had arrived, which had immediately aroused my interest. One week after the call I received only a single specimen of the "new" cichlid which had a length of 11 cm. It had a silvery coloration and a partially interrupted, diagonal line. It had a very wide mouth in which many rows of teeth were arranged to form a rasp. It was beyond doubt that this cichlid was a member of the genus *Corematodus*, to be precisely *C. taeniatus.*

The other species which is assigned to this genus is *C. shiranus*, a cichlid with faint vertical barring. Both species are known to employ a rather unusual foraging technique; they scrape small scales from the peduncles and caudal fins of other fish, mainly cichlids.

After a short acclimatization period I placed the scale-eater in a community tank with several mbuna and larger haplochromines. Already a few hours after its introduction the new inhabitant eyed with great interest the caudal fins of the other fish. The attacks mostly occurred from behind. With a feigned desinterest it would slowly approach its prey followed by a sudden bite in the caudal fin. Less common were attacks initiated swimming above the victim. The fin itself was rarely damaged but the fine scales that cover most of the haplochromine's fins made up for a seemingly nutritious meal. After a few attacks, however, the fin would show rashes and after a few days all other inhabitants of the tank had scrubbed fins. Meanwhile, the scale-eater showed a healthy appetite for the regular aquarium fare as well.

After a while the other fish gradually learned how to escape the attacks and kept a distance to the villain. Especially the mbuna proved to learn quickly. It took about two months before an acceptable balance was reached. The fins of the non-mbuna were healed and the scale-eater had switched almost entirely to the standard aquarium food.

When I introduced a few new, unexperienced cichlids in the tank they were immediately attacked by *C. taeniatus*. Since they were the only fish in the tank unaware of the scale-eater's habits they succumbed the repeated attacks a day later.

In principle it is possible to house *C. taeniatus* together with other species. Its best tankmates are mbuna or other robust species like those of the genus *Nimbochromis*.

Aulonocara rostratum Trewavas, 1935

Edwin Reitz

A wild caught male *Aulonocara rostratum* in breeding coloration. Photos by Edwin Reitz.

Until recently *Aulonocara rostratum*, which has a lake-wide distribution, was offered as *A. macrochir* in the trade, but it is now clear that both these names apply to the same species, i.e. *A. macrochir* is a synonym of *A. rostratum*.

Until 1990 only males were exported as females were difficult to find. Then, at the beginning of 1991, the first few females were exported to Europe.

After two to three weeks of acclimatisation, *A. rostratum*, like most Malawian cichlids, eats any type of aquarium fare and starts showing its splendid coloration. Although it can grow to a size of about 20 cm, it has a very small mouth. In the wild *A. rostratum* feeds in the typical *Aulonocara* fashion: it lowers its head to just above the substrate and tries to locate any prey moving in the sand. Such behaviour is only observed in some specimens in the first few weeks after importation.

A. rostratum lives over the sandy substrates of the lake where adult males dig their nests. A breeding colony of this cichlid contains several males and all of them will have constructed a deep crater-nest which is defended energetically. Therefore one should give *A. rostratum* a large tank with plenty of sand on the bottom. Interestingly, in the aquarium *A. rostratum* does not seem to construct a crater-nest. I have never seen it digging. What it does is to take away any irregularity from the spawning-site. While doing so it carries small bits of sand out of its nest each time. In the long term the spawning-site becomes a shallow, clean dip in the bottom with a diameter of about 40 cm.

The pre-spawning activity lasts much longer than in any other known Peacock. With my fish it lasts about two to three days before the actual spawning takes place. In the meantime the male continuously leads the ripe female to its nest.

The male induces the female to deposit some eggs by dragging its lavishly ornamented anal fin over the nest while the pair circle around each other. When the female deposits some eggs, up to 10 at a time, the male is parallel to the female (not in T-position). The female turns around quickly and starts picking up the eggs. Meanwhile the male has moved near the the eggs and may fertilize them while they are being picked up. The male makes another pass and again drags its anal fin over the nest. By now the female has collected all of the eggs and picks at the spots on the male's anal fin. Then the cycle is repeated. A spawning lasts about one hour.

During the incubation the female does not eat. After three weeks she releases her fry; in small females they number about 50 but in large, well-fed females spawns of about 150 fry are common.

The male drags its ornate anal fin over the spawning-site and entices the female to lay more eggs.

The female deposits up to 10 eggs at the time. ▶

After the eggs are laid, the female turns around and picks them up.

Taeniochromis holotaenia (Regan, 1922)

Peter Baasch

A male *Taeniochromis holotaenia* in breeding coloration. Photo by Peter Baasch.

Aquarists surely assess a cichlid in a different way to that used by the experienced ichthyologist, and try to "arrange" their fish according to personal points of view. The aquarist has "classified" his cichlids according their behaviour, gross morphology, and colour patterns. Other criteria were not available to the layman, while scientists applied totally different methods. Both scientist and aquarist had problems appreciating each other's standpoint. The aquarist could not understand the reasoning of the scientist, and the scientist underestimated the non-scientific approach of the aquarist. The latter could not understand that one has to measure carefully and count certain features before a classification of the particular fish could be achieved.

The revision of Malaŵian haplochromines by David Eccles and Ethelwynn Trewavas (1989), and the publications of scientists who are aquarists at the same time, have resulted in characters like morphology, pigmentation pattern, distribution, and evolutionary traits becoming accessible to the hobbyist. The development of this mutual understanding may pave the road to a better cooperation between the scientist and aquarist.

Taeniochromis holotaenia is one of those species with a unique pigmentation pattern which is crucial for its classification. It is the only species in its genus. Although a few specimens had been exported throughout the years it had never been recognized as an interesting cichlid. Now that aquarists are more aware of the complexity of the Malaŵian species flock a renewed importation of this species in September 1990 was greeted with keen interest.

From a morphological viewpoint *T. holotaenia* belongs to a group cichlids classified by aquarists as "Torpedos". Recently such cichlids have been exported much more frequently than before. Usually they are put together in an importer's tank and labeled "Haplochromis Torpedo". Among these "Torpedos" there are species from different genera, so careful selection from such collections is needed. Cichlids which are traded as "Torpedos" are e.g. *Sciaenochromis gracilis, Sc. spilostichus, Stigmatochromis* sp. "Spilostichus Type", *Champsochromis spilorhynchus, Ch. caeruleus,* and *Maravichromis formosus.* All these species are characterized by a very slender body and a diagonal line, which in some cases consists of a row of smaller spots, on the body. Among this mixture *T. holotaenia* is easily identified since it lacks the diagonal stripe.

T. holotaenia (*holo* = complete, *taenia* = stripe) is characterized by a horizontal band which connects the eye with the caudal peduncle. In addition to this distinct band a black bar runs

48

T. holotaenia in its natural habitat in Senga Bay (above) and in the aquarium. Note the difference in coloration.

horizontally between the eyes, which gives the impression of the fish being completely circumscribed by a black line. Depending on the fish's, emotions vertical bars may be present as well. This unique and remarkable pattern formed the basis of placing this species in a genus of its own, *Taeniochromis*, although it has some resemblance to species of the genus *Dimidiochromis*.

T. holotaenia seems to have a wide distribution in the lake but it also seems to be rare at most locations. The few observations made in its natural habitat were restricted to sub-adults with an average length of about 10 cm. They were seen over sand and in the intermediate habitat at a depth ranging between 10 and 20 metres. These individuals all showed a very light ground colour with the distinct black line. Spawning males, or males in breeding colours, were not seen. The observations, however, indicated that *T. holotaenia* is a pursuit hunter.

In captivity this cichlid accepts any regular type of aquarium food. The acclimatization of large adults demands a relatively long period, which seems to be common with piscivores. When kept in sufficiently large aquariums (over 200 cm) and given regular food, *T. holotaenia* adapts to its situation and "forgets" about its piscivorous nature.

Males become territorial simultaneously with the assumption of breeding coloration. The male constructs a very shallow dip in the sand as spawning-site, usually near a rock (sometimes even under one). The courting process is rather turbulent. Females with a length of about 20 cm release spawns of about 100 fry. At release the fry are small but grow quickly showing the characteristic band at an early stage in their development.

Juveniles have a silvery-yellow ground colour like their counterparts in the lake. Adults, however, show a rather dark pigmentation in the aquarium. Possibly this colour change also occurs in the lake. I shall have to wait for the moment the juveniles start changing their attire.

Male *T. holotaenia* have a sky-blue breeding colour with yellowish fins. In this respect it closely resembles *Sc. gracilis*, *Sc. spilostichus* and *St.* sp. "Spilostichus Type".

In the aquarium, compared with other cichlids of similar length and lifestyle, *T. holotaenia* behaves relatively peacefully. Maximum size is around 22 cm for males.

Lethrinops micrentodon (Regan, 1922)

Peter Baasch

A wildcaught male *Lethrinops micrentodon* from Makokola Reef.

Superficially this cichlid seems to belong to the genus *Aulonocara* rather than to *Lethrinops*. The latter genus includes many species which are aquaristically unknown but is getting more and more attention from aquarists.

Eccles and Trewavas (1989) revised the genus *Lethrinops* and described two new genera: *Taeniolethrinops* and *Tramitichromis*. Although there is now a certain logic to the systematics of this large genus, for the aquarist distinguishing the different species is still problematic. The females in particular provide a major problem because responsible breeders want to prevent hybridization by placing the "right" female with a male.

The species depicted in the photograph above has been exported only once, in spring 1990, and was identified as *Lethrinops micrentodon*. It belongs to a small group of deep-living species which have a specialized feeding behavior. Together with *L. microdon* and *L. stridei* it feeds predominantly on diatoms which have settled on the bottom of the lake. Most specimens of these three species have been collected below a depth of 50 metres and all three seem to be restricted to the southern part of the lake. The *L. micrentodon* that have been exported were collected at Makokola Reef, south of Boadzulu Island. They were found at a depth of 36 m at the border of sand and rock.

A few weeks after I had acclimatized my fish to the confines of the aquarium a male started to stake out its territory in one of the corners. The territory was demarcated by a wall of sand which had the shape of a quarter circle. The radius measured about 45 cm. If enough room had been given the entire territory would have been a complete circle with a diameter of almost one metre! The edge of the construction is just a few centimetres high. In the centre of the territory —in the case of a quarter circle in the corner— the male builds a small cone of very fine sand. This cone serves as the spawning-site.

It is not known whether *L. micrentodon* breeds throughout the year or if it has a specific breeding season. The specimens in my tank have never stopped breeding since I introduced them into the aquarium, but this behaviour is also known from other *Lethrinops* species which breed seasonally in the wild.

Females, which reach a maximum size of about 10 cm, produce 50 to 60 fry per spawn. The fry are very small at the time of release but grow rapidly. At a length of about 5 cm the males start colouring up. The maximum size of the males lies around 13 cm. *L. micrentodon* is a very attractive cichlid. It requires a small aquarium (minimum 100 cm) with a sufficient amount of fine sand to provide material for the construction of a nest.

Labeotropheus fuelleborni Ahl, 1927

A territorial male *Labeotropheus fuelleborni* at Katale Island near Chilumba.

Several geographical variants of both species of *Labeotropheus* are regularly exported and are among the popular cichlids from the lake. These two species, *L. fuelleborni* and *L. trewavasae*, live sympatrically at many locations, but hybridisation between them hardly ever occurs. I have seen a hybrid between these two species in the population at Chidunga Rocks (near Chipoka) only. As far as I know there are only two regions where males of both *L. fuelleborni* and *L. trewavasae* are entirely blue. These localities are Mara Rocks and the rocky shores near Nkhata Bay. At all other locations only one of the two species is present or the two species are differently coloured. Most rocky reefs are inhabited by *L. trewavasae* only whereas at Likoma, Chizumulu, Kande, Mbenji, Namalenje and Mumbo Island only *L. fuelleborni* is present. The rocky shores along the main coasts harbour both species.

There are three major male colour patterns known for each species. The most common for *L. fuelleborni* is entirely navy-blue with distinct barring in territorial males. *L. trewavasae* is also known in completely blue races but the variant at Nkhata Bay is cobalt-blue and may thus be distinguished from the navy-blue *L. fuelleborni* at the same location. The second colour pattern present in both species is a blue body and an orange or red dorsal fin. The third pattern consists of a yellow, orange or rusty brown coloration on the flanks, belly or dorsal part of the body. Some popula-tions of *L. fuelleborni* have a yellow or orange coloured belly or flank (see photo above of the Katale Island population). At one location both species may have an orange colour on the body. In *L. trewavasae* this colour is restricted to the upper half of the flank whereas in *L. fuelleborni* it is present on the lower half.

These three colour patterns are a part of the genetic variation of the two species. The basic colour seems to be entirely blue as this is the colour seen in almost all regions where only one of the two species is present. The presence of one of the other two patterns seems to have originated in a random fashion. It probably helped to differentiate between the two species when they came into contact (or it became the only way to differentiate). At each location the process of chance-expression of a pattern and the subsequent sexual selection developed into today's checkered distribution of the various colour patterns. The colour pattern of *L. trewavasae* varies more abruptly between adjacent populations than that of *L. fuelleborni*. *L. fuelleborni* is able to cross sandy areas in shallow water along the shoreline. *L. trewavasae* is restricted to the deeper parts of the habitat and may thus never have genetic contact with nearby populations.

Pseudotropheus saulosi Konings, 1990

Although large schools of *P. saulosi* occur, only a small part of the reef is inhabited by this mbuna.

A territorial male *Pseudotropheus saulosi*.

The reef north of Chizumulu Island, the so-called Taiwan Reef, may prove to be the most important place in Lake Malaŵi to study the evolution of the Malaŵian species flock. While most rock-dwelling cichlids have formed species complexes at most other locations, most of these complexes are represented by one species only at Taiwan Reef. The formation of a species complex elsewhere is probably due to the process of geographical isolation caused by the fluctuating water level of the lake. Due to its isolated position such processes probably did not occur at Taiwan Reef. If one explains the species complexes by the process of sympatric speciation (the creation of a new species in the presence of its ancestor), then how do we explain why that process obviously didn't occur at Taiwan Reef? Food is not a limiting factor (at present), because the reef is inhabited by thousands of rock-dwelling cichlids and is a rich fishing ground for utaka as well.

Pseudotropheus saulosi is one of the commonest cichlids on the reef and certainly the most conspicuous. Females and non-territorial males forage in large schools of sometimes more than 100 individuals. These troups move in the upper reaches of the reef while picking at the biocover. In November 1990 I could not find *P. saulosi* below a depth of 14 metres. In May 1989, it was the only species around in the upper regions of the reef while a very strong current swept over the reef. Territorial males defend a relatively large area in front of a cave, but spawning also occurred on the open substrate.

P. saulosi shows a strong sexual dichromatism, i.e. males and females have different coloration. The males start changing to their blue, zebra-like dress when they are at a size slightly short of 5 cm (2"). Their maximum size lies a little over 8.5 cm (3"). In the aquarium, however, they may grow to a size of about 10 cm. Due to its small size and vibrant coloration *P. saulosi* may become one of most popular cichlids from Lake Malaŵi.

Labidochromis sp. "Hongi"

Peter Knabe

A mature male *Labidochromis* sp. "Hongi" claims much of the space in the aquarium when kept with other males.

In 1990 during a collection expedition in Mbamba Bay, Tanzania, Hans Fleischer and Thomas Engel discovered a beautifully coloured *Labidochromis* at Hongi Island which they were able to bring back alive to Germany.

In January 1991 I was able to observe *Labidochromis* sp. "Hongi" in its natural habitat. Hongi Island, situated between Liuli and Mbamba Bay, consists of two smaller islands which contain mainly very large boulders. These two islets are separated by a 40 m wide and 8 to 12 m deep stretch of water. The biotope consists here of a sandy bottom with solitary rocks. Because the two islets consist of large boulders, large caves and overhanging ledges are frequently found underwater. In this type of habitat I was able to observe *L*. sp. "Hongi" at all levels of the rocky coast. Most individuals, however, were found at a depth of about 8 metres. There I saw 8 individuals of which three were males displaying in front of a cave. As far as I could observe they fed on plankton or nibbled form the biocover.

I also found *L*. sp. "Hongi", albeit at a lower density, at Lundo Island. Lundo is, from an aquaristic viewpoint, a very interesting island which lies between Hongi and Mbamba Bay. The shores of Lundo Island consist of small —maximum football size— rocks.

In the aquarium *L*. sp. "Hongi" behaves like most Mbuna. The two males and two females which I obtained from the first import were placed in a 1000-litre aquarium. Within one week the more dominant male spawned with both females. The spawning took place on the gravel at a rather randomly chosen site. The number of fry released after three weeks varied between seven and 18. The fry grow slowly and reach maturity after one year. The parents had a length of about 6 cm when I obtained them; after almost two years of maintenance in captivity the largest male has grown to a length of about eight centimetres. The decoration of the aquarium should have plenty of shelter for the females.

L. sp. "Hongi" in its natural habitat. Photo by Peter Knabe.

VICTORIAN CICHLIDS

Part I: Introduction to taxonomy and ecology

Ole Seehausen

A male *"Haplochromis" nyererei*, a zooplanktivorous rock dwelling cichlid.

Although the family Cichlidae is otherwise well-documented in aquaristic literature, Lake Victoria cichlids are one of the few groups which have been given little coverage.

For many decades scientific interest in these fishes was also limited (Barel *et al.*, 1991) and only a handful of ichthyologists were familiar with them. The taxonomy of Lake Victoria cichlids is still an unresolved problem. Regan, in his 1922 revision, covered 48 haplochromine species. Greenwood, in his 1979/80 revision, knew about 106, and he redistributed the former *Haplochromis* members over 15 new and re-erected

genera. Since then about 200 more species have been scientifically discovered (most of them still awaiting description), many of which bridge the gaps between the new genera (Witte, 1974). For these and other reasons (see below) many ichthyologists in the eighties preferred to refer all species back to *Haplochromis* as an interim measure.

Taxonomic classification in haplochromine cichlids was traditionally based on skull morphology and dentition. Striking similarities were found with cichlid species from the other African Great Lakes, mainly those from Lake

Malaŵi, exemplified by pairs of genera like *Macropleurodus* (Victoria) and *Chilotilapia* (Malaŵi) (Regan, 1922) and *Paralabidochromis* (Victoria) and *Labidochromis* (Malaŵi) (Greenwood, 1956a). Such observations resulted in discussions on polyphyletic versus the previously assumed mono- or oligo-phyletic nature of the lake flocks (i.e. Greenwood, 1981).

In the last decade molecular biochemical work on East African cichlids was begun and provided strong support for the idea of a monophyletic origin for the Victorian haplochromines (Sage *et al.*, 1984; Meyer *et al.*, 1990), with two exceptions being the non-endemic species *Pseudocrenilabrus multicolor* and *Astatoreochromis alluaudi*. Besides the species of Lake Victoria, the Victorian species flock includes the haplochromines of Lakes Nabugabo, Kyoga, and very probably Lakes Edward, George, and Kivu (cf. Meyer *et al.*, 1990; Greenwood, 1981 for a discussion). This flock appears to be the sister group of the Malaŵian flock and the two together apparently represent the sister group to *Astatoreochromis* (Meyer *et al.*, 1990). However, the taxonomy at lower levels remains unclear because of the extremely low genetic variability within the entire Lake Victoria flock (Meyer, pers. comm.). The striking feature in the evolution of the Victorian haplochromines is that the morphological diversity is not reflected in a profound genetic divergence. Taxonomy is further complicated by a strong genetically independent variability.

How much do we think we know about the taxonomy and phylogeny (descent) of Victorian haplochromines?

1. We have strong evidence to assume a monophyletic origin for the species flock.

2. Although species differentiation at this evolutionary level is not only difficult in practice, but also a fundamental problem (Barel *et al.*, 1991), we know of many cases in which morphologically and genetically almost identical, sympatric, and parasympatric forms, often differing only in male breeding coloration, are ecologically distinct species. In several cases it has been possible to show their ecological segregation (Hoogerhoud *et al.*, 1986; Goldschmidt *et al.*, 1990). However, this is much more difficult in isolated populations.

Why the hesitation to use Greenwood's new genera? The traditional haplochromine taxonomy is to a large extent based on the anatomy of the feeding apparatus. The members of the genus *Labrochromis* Regan, 1920 (re-erected by Greenwood in 1980), for example, share a heavy pharyngeal apparatus as the only derived feature. This was considered indicative of their monophyletic origin (Greenwood, 1980). Ecological fieldwork and experiments in the laboratory

A male *"Haplochromis" chilotes*, a large species with lobed lips that feeds mainly on insects. Photo by Ole Seehausen.

have clearly shown that (1) the elements of the feeding apparatus are phenotypically influenced by environmental factors (eg. type of prey) (Witte, 1984; Hoogerhoud, 1986), (2) many groups described on the basis of the anatomy of the feeding apparatus and the connected skull architecture are in effect ecological groups. This does not necessarily deny their validity as taxonomic units but it is quite possible that parallel evolution has occurred, producing superficially similar species whose derived characters are convergent rather than synapomorphic (features with an identical origin which species of the group have in common). Another reason for the hesitation is that many species have morphological characters which fall in between those of two or more of Greenwood's lineages making it impossible to delimit genera (cf. Hoogerhoud, 1984; Witte, 1987).

With the background of the extreme difficulties in identifying and classifying Victorian haplochromines on the one hand, and the increasing need to do so for adequate fisheries management on the other, researchers from Leiden University worked out the concept of trophic groups (Witte & Van Oijen, 1990) which allows an ecological classification of haplochromine species without any phylogenetic implications. Members of a trophic group are using the same food category. However, this does not mean that they are feeding exclusively on the same prey; food choice can differ seasonally as well as during the 24 hours of the day. To identify the trophic status of a series of specimens usually a combination of ecological and morphological information has to be considered.

Witte and Van Oijen (1990) further pointed out that morphological characters correlate more closely with the way in which the food is collected than with the food type itself. Molluscivores, for instance, which crush snails between their pharyngeals, are morphologically much closer to some insectivores which also need a strong pharyngeal apparatus, than to other molluscivores which pull snails out of their shells with their oral teeth. In such cases Witte and Van Oijen departed from the strict trophic classification and recognized subtrophic groups on the basis of feeding techniques. However, in many cases the actual manner in which the fish obtains its food is unknown, and it is obvious that the insectivores, for instance, will have to be divided into several subtrophic groups once enough information is available. It is my intention to introduce the trophic groups in a series of articles and to discuss parts of the Victorian *Haplochromis* fauna on this basis.

I believe that trophic/ecological identification of Victorian cichlids provides the aquarist with information on his/her fish which is more valuable than that which can be gained from unreliable taxonomic (pseudo)identifications which are often no more than the result of guessing. At this point I believe it is necessary to stress the fact that identification of Lake Victoria cichlids by coloration alone is impossible unless one is very familiar with the very species in question and even then mistakes are difficult to avoid unless other characters are checked.

Lake Victoria is just one of at least six East African cichlid lakes and, being a shallow water body —maximum depth about 90 m— with a huge surface area of approximately 69,000 km² it differs considerably in its geography from Lakes Malaŵi and Tanganyika.

Comparison of the faunas of the different lakes is an intriguing approach that can provide valuable information. However, such investi-gations have been few (Fryer & Iles, 1972; Greenwood, 1981; Witte, 1984; Ribbink & Eccles, 1988) because concrete data allowing direct comparisons are still scarce, and recent work on Lake Victoria has shown that statements based on meagre data have produced an incorrect picture in the past (Fryer & Iles, 1972 versus Witte, 1984 and Dorit, 1986). Only a few words will be added here on aspects of endemism, speciosity, and trophic composition of the flocks.

Until quite recently it was believed that Lake Victoria cichlids, in contrast to those of Lakes Malaŵi and Tanganyika, exhibit neither geographic restriction nor geographic variation (Fryer & Iles, 1972; Greenwood, 1974). The work of the Haplochromis Ecology Survey Team (HEST) in the south of the lake has shown that this hypothesis does not hold (Witte, 1984). Several examples of intraspecific geographic variation were encountered (Dorit, 1986; Witte & Witte-Maas, 1987) and only a minority of the species has a lake-wide distribution (Witte, 1984).

Fryer & Iles (1972) further emphasized that Victorian cichlids were ecologically less restricted and specialized when compared to those of the other two lakes. Recent research proves otherwise. Pronounced ecological segregation and habitat restriction was found in many cases involving the following criteria (after Witte, 1984): bottom type preference; vertical distribution along the bottom profile; vertical distribution in the water column; qualitative differences in food composition, including food size partitioning; quantitative differences in food composition; differences in food collection strategy; and partitioning of spawning areas. I would like to

An orange blotched female of a new species from the *"H". nigricans*-group, an epilithic scraper. Photos by Ole Seehausen.

add behaviour (Seehausen, 1991a).

Even within the geographically very restricted area of a single bay (Van Oijen, 1981; Barel *et al.*, 1991; pers. obs.) one encounters completely different species assemblages correlated with substrate type and vegetation.

I believe that the comparisons of the speciosity of the Great Lakes species flocks which have been published over the years merely reflected the state of knowledge at the time of publication. According to Ribbink & Eccles (1988) and Konings (1989) about 400 haplochromine cichlids are known from Lake Malaŵi. Of these about 50% are rock dwelling forms (Mbuna) with an often very limited geographical distribution. For a comparison with the Victorian fauna one has to consider that the existence of a group of rock-dwelling cichlids similar to Mbuna in Lake Victoria has been known only since 1981 (Van Oijen *et al.*). At that time at least 16 rock frequenting taxa were known from the northern part of the Mwanza Gulf alone. Sampling was carried out at rock stations by Sevenster, Bouton, Fermon, and by myself during the last five years and has revealed many more rock frequenting cichlids within this small region of the lake. In addition we collected several apparently endemic forms at small off-shore islands outside the gulf. Ribbink and Eccles (1988) found communities of

"H". nigricans from an off-shore, deep-bodied population, representing the biter type in *Haplochromis*.

"H". cf. *altigenis*, one of the larger piscivores which are almost extinct, representing the sucker type in *Haplochromis*.

57

9 to 14 rock dwelling cichlid species at small isolated rocky outcrops in Lake Malaŵi. This number corresponds well with our findings at similar places in Lake Victoria. While being aware that it is risky to draw conclusions from results of geographically restricted work, it appears likely to me that, conservatively calculated, more than 200 rock dwelling cichlid forms —many having a very restricted distribution— are to be expected in Lake Victoria. Ribbink and Eccles (*op. cit.*) reported circa 180 haplochromine cichlid species found in a Malaŵian trawl survey of more than 70 stations ranging in depth from 18 to 180 m. Van Oijen *et al.* (1981) found circa 200 species in a Victorian trawl survey of an area covering 45 km² in the Mwanza Gulf which has a maximum depth of only 16 m. I can see little evidence to assume that the Victorian fauna was less speciose than the currently known fauna of Lake Malaŵi. Unfortunately it is no longer possible to prove this because of the impact of predation by the introduced *Lates* sp. on the flock.

Due to the patchy information a comparison of the cichlid flocks on trophic level is also difficult. The picture of the trophic composition of the Victorian flock has changed considerably since 1922 and this change shows rather steadily continuing developments: a relative decrease in large species (i.e. piscivores) and a relative increase in small pelagic or semi-pelagic species (i.e. planktivores), deep water species and Aufwuchs feeders. This probably reflects the sampling of the species, which is affected by the fishing techniques employed by researchers. Taking the expected increase in rock frequenting cichlids (mainly algae scrapers and insectivores) into account, the otherwise pronounced difference between the Victorian and Malaŵian flocks would be reduced considerably. However, the high percentage of piscivores in the original (pre-*Lates*) community remains an outstanding feature of the Victorian flock.

Much of the public and scientific discussion that has arisen about Lake Victoria during the last years relates to the enormous impact of the introduction of the nile perch (*Lates* sp.) on the indigenous fauna (Barel, 1986; Witte *et al.*, 1991). It can be said without doubt that the vast majority of the sublittoral and open water species have declined drastically —about 60% of them have not been found for several years— and that the littoral fauna is affected to a lesser degree (Witte *et al.*, 1991; Seehausen, *in prep.*). It is apparent that the speed and degree of the decline differed between ecological groups. Relevant factors are habitat, adult size and abundancy of a species (Witte *et al.*, 1991). Some details concerning the different cichlid groups will be given in following articles.

View of a habitat; rocks and papyrus are often adjacent.

View of a rocky habitat under water: grazing "H". sp. "Velvet Black".

An adult *Lates* sp. caught by bottom trawl in the Mwanza Gulf. Photos by Ole Seehausen

References

BAREL, C.D.N. (1986) Endemische Cichliden des Viktoriasees vor dem Aussterben. *DCG-info*, 17 (3).

BAREL, C.D.N., LIGTVOET, W., GOLDSCHMIDT, T., WITTE, F. & GOUDSWAARD, P.C. (1991) The haplochromine cichlids in Lake Victoria: an assessment of biological and fisheries interests. In: Keenleyside, M.H.A. (Ed.), *Cichlid fishes, behaviour, ecology and evolution.* Chapman & Hall, London.

DORIT, R.L. (1986) *Molecular and morphological variation in Lake Victoria haplochromine cichlids (Perciformes: Cichlidae).* Ph.D. diss. Harvard, Cambridge, Mass.

FRYER, G. & ILES, T.D. (1972) *The cichlid fishes of the Great Lakes of Africa.* Oliver & Boyd, Edinburgh.

GOLDSCHMIDT, T., WITTE, F. & DE VISSER, J. (1990) Ecological segregation in zooplanktivorous haplochromine species (Pisces: Cichlidae) from Lake Victoria. *Oikos* (Copenhagen) 58; pp 343-355.

GREENWOOD, P.H. (1965) Environmental effects on the pharyngeal mill of a cichlid fish, *Astatoreochromis alluaudi* and their taxonomic implications. *Proc. Linn. Soc. Lond.* 176; 1-10.

GREENWOOD, P.H. (1974) The cichlid fishes of Lake Victoria, East Africa: the biology and evolution of a species flock. *Bull. Br. Mus. Nat. Hist. (Zool.)* Suppl. 6.

GREENWOOD, P.H. (1981) *The haplochromine fishes of the East African lakes.* Kraus-Thomson Organization, Munich. (Includes all the cited papers in reprint unless given separately)

HOOGERHOUD, R.J.C. (1984) A taxonomic reconsideration of the haplochromine genera *Gaurochromis* Greenwood, 1980 and *Labrochromis* Regan, 1920 (Pisces: Cichlidae). *Neth. J. Zool.* 34; pp 539-565.

HOOGERHOUD, R.J.C. (1986) *Ecological morphology of some cichlid fishes.* Ph.D. Thesis, Leiden, Netherlands.

HOOGERHOUD, R.J.C., WITTE, F., & BAREL, C.D.N. (1983) The ecological differentiation of two closely resembling *Haplochromis* species from Lake Victoria. *Neth. J. Zool.* 33; pp 283-305.

MEYER, A., KOCHER, T.D., BASASIBWAKI, P. & WILSON, A.C. (1990) Monophyletic origin of Lake Victoria cichlid fishes suggested by mitochondrial DNA sequences. *Nature* 347; pp 550-553.

OIJEN, M.J.P. van, WITTE, F., & WITTE-MAAS, E.L.M. (1981) An introduction to ecological and taxonomic investigations on the haplochromine cichlids from the Mwanza Gulf of Lake Victoria. *Neth. J. Zool.* 31; pp 149-174.

REGAN, C.T. (1922) The cichlid fishes of Lake Victoria. *Proc. Zool. Soc. Lond.*; pp 157-191.

RIBBINK, A.J. & ECCLES, D.H. (1988) Fish communities in the East African Great Lakes. In: C. Léveque, M.N. Bruton & G.W. Sentongo (Eds.) *Biology and ecology of African freshwater fishes.* ORSTOM, Paris.

SAGE, R.D., LOISELLE, P.V., BASASIBWAKI, P., & WILSON, A.C. (1984) Molecular versus morphological change among cichlid fishes of Lake Victoria. In: A.A. Echelle & I. Kornfield (Eds.) *Evolution of species flocks.* University of Maine at Orono Press.

SEEHAUSEN, O. (1991a) A comparison of some ethological aspects of reproductive ecology in three zooplanktivorous and one generalized insectivorous *Haplochromis* from Lake Victoria. *7th Intl. Ichthyol. Congress (The Hague); Bull. zool. Mus. Univ. Amsterdam.*, special issue, August 1991.

SEEHAUSEN, O. (1991b) Die zooplanktivoren Cichliden des Viktoriasees. *DATZ*, 44; pp 715-721.

WITTE, F. (1984a) Consistency and functional significance of morphological differences between wild-caught and domestic *Haplochromis squamipinnis* (Pisces: Cichlidae). *Neth. J. Zool.* 34; pp 596-612.

WITTE, F. (1984b) Ecological differentiation in Lake Victoria haplochromines: comparison of cichlid species flocks in African lakes. In: A.A. Echelle & I. Kornfield (Eds.) *Evolution of species flocks.* University of Maine at Orono Press.

WITTE, F., GOLDSCHMIDT, T, WANINK, J., Van OIJEN, M., GOUDSWAARD, K. & LIGTVOET, W. (1991) Species extinction and ecological changes in Lake Victoria. *Proc. 7th Intl. Ichthyol. Congress (The Hague)*, in press.

WITTE, F. & Van OIJEN, M.J.P. (1990) Taxonomy, ecology and fishery of Lake Victoria haplochromine trophic groups. *Zool. Verh. (Natl. Nat. Hist. Mus. Leiden)* 262.

WITTE, F. & WITTE-MAAS, E.L.M. (1987) Implications for taxonomy and functional morphology of intraspecific variation in haplochromine cichlids of Lake Victoria. In: F. Witte. *From form to fishery* Ph.D. Thesis, Leiden, Netherlands.

WEST AFRICAN CICHLIDS

Lamprologus sp. "Kinganga"

Frank Warzel

This *Lamprologus*, for once not one of the many new species from Lake Tanganyika, was collected by Heiko Bleher during one of his many collecting expeditions in Africa. The male shown in the photographs, which is the only specimen of this species collected thus far, was caught in the Lower Zaïre (Congo River) near Kinganga about 200 km downstream from the Zaïrean capital, Kinshasa.

The Lower Zaïre at Kinganga had been the site of an earlier expedition by ichthyologists about twenty years ago. An American expedition led by Tyson Roberts and Donald Stewart collected many species of fish here in 1973. Three years later both scientists published the results of their expedition and in one of the many plates accompanying the publication a small cichlid is depicted with the caption *Lamprologus werneri*. The type species of *L. werneri* (Poll, 1959: 108-109, Pl. XIX), however, was collected in the lower part of Malebo Pool, a very shallow, lake-like widening of the lower Zaïre river. Malebo Pool is a frequently visited site where exporters collect their aquarium fishes. As well as *Steatocranus casuarius* (Buffalo Head Cichlid), which is regularly exported in large quantities from this

The cranial gibbosity of the male *Lamprologus* sp. "Kinganga" is an interesting feature. Photos by Frank Warzel.

Lamprologus sp. "Kinganga", hopefully not the only importation.

area, *L. wemeri*, usually under trade names like "Lamprologus Congoensis" or "Lamprologus Congolensis", has also found its way into many aquaria. Although this cichlid closely resembles the "new" *Lamprologus* sp. "Kinganga", especially in its cylindrical shape, there are a number of minor differences which suggest that we are dealing with a distinct species and not with a geographical variant of one species, namely *Lamprologus wemeri*.

The male *Lamprologus* sp. "Kinganga" that I kept for several years in one of my aquaria, grew to a length of about 10 cm, which is several centimetres shorter than the maximum length known for *L. wemeri*. The pattern of light spots on the dorsal and caudal fins is much brighter in *Lamprologus* sp. "Kinganga" than in *L. wemeri*. Also the vertical markings on the dorsal part of the body are narrower compared to those in *L. wemeri*.

The relatively large cranial gibbosity of the "new" species and the distinct markings on the scales may be further, possibly typical, characteristics of this species.

Roberts and Stewart noted in their earlier quoted publication that they too found differences between these cichlids, and consequently treated both forms as possible geographical variants of *L. wemeri*.

As an aquarium inhabitant *Lamprologus* sp. "Kinganga" is an undemanding, sometimes territorial cichlid which accepts regular aquarium fare and tolerates any type of water with no noticeable distress. Even larger fishes find it difficult to intimidate this small cichlid; typical *Lamprologus*.

References

POLL, M (1959) Recherches sur la faune ichthyologique de la région du Stanley Pool. *Annls. Mus. r. Congo Belge. Ser 8°, Sci. Zool.* 71; pp 75-174, pls. XII-XXVI.
ROBERTS, T.R. & STEWART, D.J. (1976) An ecological and systematic survey of fishes in the rapids of the lower Zaïre or Congo River. *Bull. Mus. Comp. Zool.* 147, N° 6; pp 239-317.
WARZEL, F. (1990) Ein neuer *Lamprologus* aus dem unteren Zaire? *DATZ* (43), 2; pp 74-75.

Tilapia tholloni (Sauvage, 1884)

Jan 't Hooft

The fact that the African cichlids of the genus *Tilapia*, and the closely related genera *Sarotherodon* and *Oreochromis*, are relatively poorly represented in aquaristic literature can be explained by their generally large adult size and often destructive behaviour in the aquarium. Tilapiines, however, are very interesting and I will describe my experiences with one of the most beautiful among them.

Tilapia tholloni was described by Sauvage in 1884 under the name *Chromis tholloni*, honouring the collector Tholon. Boulenger (1899) placed it in the genus *Tilapia* where it remains today.

T. tholloni is widespread in West Africa and is found in Gabon, Congo Republic, the southern part of Cameroun, and in a part of Zaïre. It is also found in the brackish waters of coastal lagoons although the water of the rivers and streams in which most individuals are found contains very few minerals. Obviously the water chemistry plays an unimportant role.

T. tholloni belongs to the vegetarians in the family Cichlidae. Examinations of stomach contents reveal predominantly remains of plants supplemented with insect-larvae and crustaceans. Two other species in the genus have a similar vegetarian diet. These are *T. zillii* and *T. rendalli*. These three cichlids have a non-overlapping distribution in most parts of Africa (Thys van den Audenaerde, 1963; see map).

The specimens I kept in the aquarium were collected by friends of mine in the Congo Republic. The juveniles, with a length of about three centimetres, were captured in a swampy area just south of the Alima River, a tributary of the Zaïre (Congo), not far from the village of Oyo. The water had a depth of 30-60 cm and the small tilapias could be collected with a handnet from among the grassy vegetation.

After I had introduced four of them in a metre-long aquarium they immediately showed their vegetarian nature. Within a few days they had completely eaten a thick layer of duckweed which had covered the water in the tank. Then they started, selectively, on the other plants in the tank. Some plants like *Anubias, Ceratophyllum*, and *Nuphar lutea* were left untouched, but soft-leaved plants were devoured in days. I fed them lettuce leaves and from time to time mosquito larvae and *Mysis*.

The juvenile *T. tholloni* had a silvery coloration with an occasional horizontal line of small spots. At a few months old, at a size of about six to seven centimetre, they changed colour. A brown colour with a greenish hue covered the once silvery body. They were then placed in a 200 cm-long aquarium in which they changed colour again at a size of about 10 cm and an estimated age of about nine months. The change consisted of the appearance of a red colour on throat and belly. Shortly after this colour change one of the four showed a further, this time drastic change in colour and behaved territorially. Its territory included more than half of the tank. A few days later a larger individual was allowed in its territory and this specimen also adopted the breeding coloration.

Previous reports (Schuitema, 1963; Nieuwenhuizen, 1967) describe the construction of large spawning pits in which eggs are laid, but in my tank the pair spawned before a pit was dug. One day after the second individual entered the territory the female had attached a large batch of eggs onto a piece of bogwood. The pair took turns fanning the eggs and dug a large pit. Four days after deposition the eggs hatched and the larvae were removed to the pit. The wriggling mass was protected by both parents.

In the meantime the remaining two fishes formed a pair as well and spawned within a few days of the first pair. This pair too started digging after

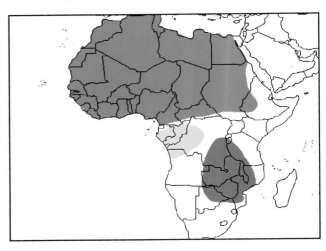

The distribution patterns of *T. tholloni* (yellow), *T. rendalli* (red) and *T. zillii* (blue).

A female *T. tholloni* fanning her eggs. Photos by Jan 't Hooft.

the eggs were deposited. The spawns of these young couples numbered more than 500 fry.

For months on end the two pairs spawned. Eggs were always stuck onto a smooth vertical substrate and the nursery-pit was always dug one day after spawning.

The four *T. tholloni* reached a size of about 18 cm before I gave them away. The maximum size of this species may be close to 25 cm.

The question is whether this cichlid, under natural circumstances, deposits eggs onto a hard, smooth surface or digs a pit in which the eggs are deposited on the bottom. Maybe the spawning method is dependent on environmental factors and both methods are practised.

A juvenile *T. tholloni* showing its silvery coloration.

An adult *T. tholloni* with neutral coloration.

References

NIEUWENHUIZEN, A. van den (1967) *Tilapia tholloni*. *Het Aquarium*. 38; pp 158-164.
SAUVAGE, H.E. (1884) Note sur les poissons de Franceville, Haut Ogooué. *Bull. Soc. zool. Fr.* 9; pp 193-198.
SCHUITEMA, A.K. (1963) *Tilapia tholloni*. *Het Aquarium*. 34; pp 83-85.
THYS van den AUDENAERDE, D.F.E. (1963) La distribution géographique des Tilapia au Congo. *Bull. Acad. r. Sci. Outre-mer*. 9; pp 570-605.

A pair of wild caught *Tilapia tholloni* guarding their fry.

Thoracochromis demeusii (Boulenger, 1899)

Martin Geerts

The African cichlid fauna can be split up into two main geographical groups: a West African group which, aquaristically seen, is dominated by *Chromidotilapia*-like cichlids and a East African group dominated by haplochromine and lamprologine cichlids. Greenwood (1987, in *Bull. Brit. Mus. nat. Hist. (Zool)* 53 (3): 200) wrote that the chromidotilapiine cichlids are adapted to habitats with flowing water, whereas the haplochromines are noted for their trophic specialisations. Although chromidotilapiine cichlids are absent from East Africa, the geographical separation of the two groups is not absolute. This is clearly shown by the cichlid fauna of the lower Zaïre. Here several haplochromine cichlids have adopted a rheophilic life style. The species to which these cichlids belong were revised in 1964 by D. Thys van den Audenaerde, who recognized four different species: *Haplochromis fasciatus, H. demeusi, H. bakongo* and *H. polli*. In his subsequently contested revision, Greenwood (1979) placed the first three species in *Thoracochromis* and the last in *Ctenochromis*. Two of these species have been introduced into the hobby.

Ctenochromis polli (Thys v. d. Audenaerde, 1964) was first introduced in the early seventies. At that time it was known under the name "Pelvicachromis Polli" which suggests that aquarists at that time didn't expect haplochromine cichlids in West Africa.

Ct. polli is only found in the old basin of Malebo Pool (Stanley Pool). Earlier authors have regarded their specimens, which were caught in the Pool, as representatives of *Th. fasciatus*.

The maximum length of *Ct. polli* males amounts to approximately 10 cm. Females remain a little smaller. The anal fin of the male shows only a single egg-spot, which was a reason for certain aquarists to experiment with this species in order to find out the function of the spot. The single egg-spot could easily be removed, but investigations indicated that it played no major role at the fertilisation of the eggs.

Thoracochromis demeusii (Boulenger, 1899), the West African Humphead, was introduced only recently into the aquaristic hobby. According to Mayland (1989, *Das Aquarium* 244: 613) the Humphead was collected by Heiko Bleher in the lower Zaïre near a village called Kiganga. Male *Th. demeusii* grow to a size of at least 14 cm (Mayland, *Cichliden Afrikas*: 17-18). Adult males have a cranial gibbosity which led the British ichthyologist Charles Tate Regan to place this cichlid in the genus *Cyphotilapia*.

Since its introduction it has been spawned in the aquarium. Its breeding behaviour is typical of a haplochromine mouthbrooder.

A wild caught male *Thoracochromis demeusii* from Kiganga, Zaïre.

CENTRAL AMERICAN CICHLIDS

The *"Cichlasoma" labridens*-complex

Juan Miguel Artigas Azas

The Pánuco river system, México's second largest Atlantic drainage and one of the most beautiful found in the country, has been pouring its entire flow for thousands of years into the Gulf of México. A beautiful assemblage of cichlids of the Parapetenia section of the genus *Cichlasoma* are endemic to the Pánuco basin. One of the species is of uncertain descent and has a restricted range: *"Cichlasoma" bartoni* from the Rio Verde valley in the western part of the basin. The other species can be placed into two groups, the first associated with *"C." carpinte* and the second with *"C." labridens*.

At present three species in the *labridens*-complex are scientifically described. *"C." labridens* was first described as *Heros labridens* by the ichthyologist Pellegrin in 1903 from specimens collected by professor Alfredo Duges of the Mexican University of Guanajuato in the Rio Verde near the city of the same name. The type locality, however, was stated as Huasteca Potosina, the name of a large part of the Rio Pánuco basin. Pellegrin also added Guanajuato to Huasteca Potosina as a type locality, something which is clearly a mistake (there are no cichlid fishes native to Guanajuato state).

The waterfalls at Tamasopo form a boundary in the distribution of some cichlids. All photos by Juan Miguel Artigas Azas.

In 1983 Jeffrey N. Taylor and Robert Rush Miller described "C." pantostictum and gave re-descriptions of "C." steindachneri and "C." labridens. The re-description of the last species was based on a group of labridens forms which were collected at over fifty different locations in the Pánuco system. Dr. Robert Rush Miller (pers. comm.) plans to describe another species in this group, the one known as the Tamasopo Labridens. This labridens lives in the isolated Río Gallinas in the mid-western part of the system.

An estimated twelve thousand years ago the valley of Río Verde —about 10,000 km² of dry land full of interesting endemic flora and fauna and situated 1000 metres above sea level— was the site of a large lake. In the course of time, either erosion or tectonic activity caused this lake to drain to the Gulf, leaving behind a large swampy area where primitive man is known to have hunted mammoths.

Over the years the swamp almost dried out, leaving small swampy regions scattered over the area. These small swamps survived thanks to the warm water springs that feed them. The swamps are isolated from one other, but contain what used to be the fauna of the prehistoric lake. Two cichlids, namely "C." bartoni and "C." labridens, share their natural habitat in those springs with several other species of fishes. The latter is the so-called Yellow Labridens.

"C." labridens feeds exclusively on crustaceans and snails which it finds in the sand and detritus on the bottom of the springs. It has well-developed, molariform pharyngeal teeth with which it can crush its prey without problem.

This cichlid, which has a marked ability to change colours according to its mood, makes an almost religious ceremony of feeding time by changing its normally yellowish coloration to a dark, sometimes velvety black pattern with a sprinkling of blue. But this habit of changing colours reaches its maximum when the fish starts breeding, which,

due to the very stable environment of the springs, takes place throughout the year. A peak in breeding activity is noted from December to March. A canary yellow and velvety black colour pattern then adorns "C." labridens and this change makes it one of the most delightful sights among the New World cichlids (see photo in *Cichlids Yearbook*, vol. 1: 75).

Pairs then look for a solid surface on which to lay their eggs. Something that would be an easy task in a river, but not in the springs where stones are scarce. Frequently stems or leaves of water lillies serve as a spawning substrate. Once a site has been chosen and thoroughly cleaned, hundred of large —about three millimetres long— orange eggs are laid, fertilized, and fanned for two days. After the eggs have hatched the larvae are transported to a large pre-dug pit below the spawning site. From then on it takes another five days before the larvae become free-swimming fry. Pairs will then protect their fry in a ferocious way. The food, in the form of organic detritus, is provided by the female by wagging her entire body in the sediment. This causes a cloud of debris in which the fry will greedily forage. The pair take the fry on foraging trips through

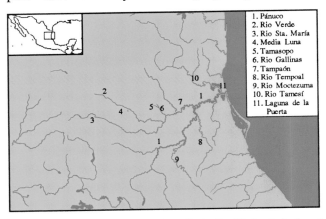

1. Pánuco
2. Rio Verde
3. Rio Sta. María
4. Media Luna
5. Tamasopo
6. Rio Gallinas
7. Tampaón
8. Rio Tempoal
9. Rio Moctezuma
10. Rio Tamesí
11. Laguna de la Puerta

The distribution of "C." labridens (2, 3, 4), "C." steindachneri (5), "C." sp. "Labridens Tamasopo" (5, 6), "C." sp. "Labridens Blue" (7, 8, 9, 10) and "C." pantostictum (11).

"C." labridens from the Rio Verde.

A natural hybrid between "C." carpinte and "C." labridens.

the habitat, interrupted every now and then by outbreaks of potential danger in the form of predators or a curious human cichlid lover. At such moments the male will either face the intruder or, if it is too big, flee away. The female will then call her fry and all will hide under the leaves of water lillies until the danger disappears. At dusk as well shelter is found among the lillies. Not until the fry have reached two to three centimetres in length, do they start making solitary foraging trips, and gradually those that survive will leave their parents. At this point they stay close to the overhanging vegetation along the shores of the channels which supplies them with shelter. Juveniles are also commonly seen around feeding adults where they may learn the technique of stirring up the sediment and, while watching, benefit from uncovered small snails or other invertebrates that the adults won't consider. *"C." labridens* and *"C." bartoni* share the habitat, ignoring each other most of the time. This is perhaps due to the fact that no direct feeding competition exists between them. *"C." bartoni*, which has conical pharyngeal teeth, feeds upon algae on the surface of waterlilly leaves or other smooth surfaces, or on zooplankton. The ratio between both species, however, is overwhelmingly on the side of *"C." bartoni* and, in fact, the yellow *labridens* from the springs, although present in all

of them, may be considered rare.

Medialuna spring, the largest of the Rio Verde valley swamps, presents additional problems for the fishes. Man-made irrigation canals, called "asequias", have been dug from this spring since the seventeenth century. A large concrete canal that feeds a network of smaller ones was built by the government in 1977 to take advantage of the large flow of the spring. The new channel intersects the Rio Verde where a different fish fauna thrives. During the rainy season the river may overflow and mix with the spring water in the canal. In this way fishes from the spring can get into the river and vice versa. *"C." carpinte* has thus colonized the canal and, although it does not do very well in the spring, it has hybridized with the yellow *labridens*. Moreover it presents an additional threat to spring cichlids as juvenile *carpinte* prey upon fry of the endemic species.

Sarotherodon species have also been introduced to the springs as a food fish. It was feared that they could pose a threat to the naturally occurring cichlids, but with the passage of time I have observed their numbers decreasing. In some springs they have completely vanished.

The Rio Verde *labridens* is very similar to the one found in the springs. It differs mainly in body morphology, having a more rounded profile and a shallower head. It has, however, the same

A pair *"C."* sp. "Labridens Tamasopo" guarding their fry under the waterfall at Tamasopo.

"C." sp. "Labridens Tamasopo" stirring the sediment.

A male "C." sp. "Labridens Blue" from the Rio Pujal.

"C." steindachneri is the largest cichlid in the Pánuco.

A natural "C." steindachneri x Tamasopo Labridens hybrid.

breeding coloration. The habitat in the Rio Verde is rather different from that found in the springs. While in the springs the labridens are used to very slow flowing water with stable temperatures from around 28° C to 32° C and good visibility, the river has moderately fast-flowing water —the labridens' preferred habitat— and significant fluctuations in water level and temperature (from 18° C to 28° C). The visibility in the river is rarely over two metres and food is plentiful.

The "C." labridens in the river feed on invertebrates which they collect in a similar way to their counterparts in the springs. The breeding season is limited to the months of March through June. Breeding stops when heavy rains cause much higher water levels with an accompanying decrease in visibility and a lower temperature.

As a spawning site, males of the yellow labridens dig a cave with a depth and width of about 10 to 15 cm at the base of a rock. One of the cave's walls is cleaned and prepared as a spawning substratum. The rest of the breeding behaviour of the river labridens matches that of their counterparts in the springs.

The yellow labridens is distributed over the western part of the Rio Verde drainage, in the Verde and Santa María rivers. This area is situated partly at an altitude of 1000 m above sea level, upstream of the confluence of the two rivers. It is also found in the drainage of this area, the Rio Tampaón, until geographical barriers in the form of waterfalls prevent migration further downstream in the system.

Downstream in the Tampaón river the 102 m high Tamul waterfall provides an effective way of isolating a unique fish fauna in the Rio Gallinas.

Two cichlids from the labridens-group live in this stream in a peculiar and close relationship. One of them is "C." steindachneri, described by Jordan and Snyder in 1900 and with a stated type locality of Rio Gallinas near the town of Rascon; the other is the so called Tamasopo labridens, a so far undescribed species.

"C." steindachneri is a large, slender cichlid with a long snout and large conical teeth. It is a piscivore and frequently hunts livebearers and tetras. On the other hand, "C." sp. "Labridens Tamasopo" is somewhat smaller, with molariform pharyngeal teeth and a rounded profile. It feeds on invertebrates and collects them in the same fashion as described for "C." labridens. The estimated ratio between the two species is about 100 Labridens for each "C." steindachneri.

The Rio Gallinas is characterized by its clear

A female "Cichlasoma" pantostictum in breeding coloration (from Laguna de la Puerta).

A male "C." pantostictum in normal dress.

Laguna de la Puerta, the type locality of "C." pantostictum.

and well-oxygenated water (pH 7.6; 100° DH!) and has a temperature ranging between 16° and 28° C.

"C."steindachneri can be found only in the Rio Agua Buena, between the waterfalls at Tamasopo and the town of Tambaca, and in Rio Ojo Frio as far as its confluence with the Rio Agua Buena, where both rivers merge to form the Rio Gallinas. The Tamasopo Labridens exceeds that range to the headwaters of the Rio Tamasopo, above the waterfalls. This may suggest that the labridens arrived before "C."steindachneri in the Rio Gallinas.

Both species breed from December to June with a peak in activity in March. During this period the pairs dig caves between the rocks and breed like the yellow "C."labridens in the Rio Verde. The only difference is the colour of the eggs which is yellowish instead of orange. Mated pairs of the Tamasopo Labridens have a minimum size of about ten centimetres for males and seven for females. In contrast, "C." steindachneri forms pairs only when the male is larger than twenty and the female larger than fifteen centimetres.

The breeding coloration of the two species also differs. The Tamasopo Labridens has a black and white chess-board pattern with a white forehead. "C." steindachneri hardly changes its coloration.

Interestingly, hybrids of the two cichlids exist. A pair consisting of a male steindachneri and a female Tamasopo Labridens was photographed underwater by Ad Konings in March 1991. This explains the occurrence of numerous fishes that have a shape in between the two, and these are only found below the Tamasopo waterfalls where both species live together.

"C." steindachneri is the largest cichlid in the Pánuco system, in some cases growing to over 40 cm in size. In some exceptional cases Tamasopo Labridens males can grow to over 30 cm in length but most large males average around 20 cm.

Downstream in the Tampaón river and in the lowland drainage of the Pánuco (including the Tamesi river, the Pánuco's northern branch, and the Moctezuma and Tempoal rivers, the southern ones), lives a different form of the labridens-complex which is known as the Blue Labridens. It is distributed over a wide area including some small rivers to the south that do not belong to the Pánuco system.

The behaviour of the Blue Labridens is almost identical to that of the previous two labridens. It prefers fast-flowing water with rock-strewn floors for feeding. The breeding coloration consists of a blue pattern and a red edge on the dorsal and anal fins. The scaleless blotch behind the pectoral fin, a common feature of all species in this group, is blood-red instead of the dark-purple observed in all others.

"C." pantostictum lives in isolated coastal lagoons near the Pánuco mouth. Its habitat is very different from those in which the other species of the labridens-group are found. The type specimens were collected in the coastal lagoons "Laguna de la Puerta" and "Laguna del Chairel" (type locality), both located near the city of Tampico. The lagoons are murky with a very low visibility of usually less than half a metre; the bottoms are always muddy. In lagoons with clear water and sandy bottoms "C." pantostictum could not be found. The temperature of the water in the lagoons, which is slightly salty, varies from around 15° C to 28° C.

"C." pantostictum —its specific name means "spotted all over"— differs from the other labridens forms by having its entire body covered with small brown spots. Such spots can also be found in the Blue Labridens, but to a much lesser degree.

The shape of "C." pantostictum resembles most closely that of the "C." labridens of the Rio Verde valley. This may not surprise us given the similarity of the bottoms from which they feed and the almost stagnant water of their habitats.

The breeding coloration shows the pattern of the labridens-complex, but this time is all black with a white forehead. Its breeding habits are difficult to assess because of the murky water in which it lives. I have collected "C." pantostictum in breeding colours from April to June. This cichlid, which grows to over 25 cm in length, has already been spawned in captivity by Don Danko (Cleveland, Ohio).

An interesting note about "C." pantostictum is that two specimens were collected in the head waters of the Rio Sabinas in the upper part of the Tamesi drainage. They seemed to live together with the Blue Labridens (Darnell, 1962). Whether they were "C." pantostictum or somewhat more spotted specimens of the Blue Labridens remains to be seen. I could not find "C." pantostictum in the Rio Sabinas or in other affluents of the Rio Tamesi.

Of all the species in the labridens-complex, in my own experience "C." pantostictum is the most aggressive one. All these species require a tank over five hundred litres and can be housed with other large "Cichlasoma". Fishes that are too big to fit their mouths, except in the case of "C." steindachneri, are normally ignored outside breeding times. The large predator of the group will be pleased with all the small fish you can provide. "C." steindachneri is also the least aggressive of the group.

The foregoing should have given a picture of the current status of the "C." labridens complex. Many questions remain as to whether these forms are to be regarded as different species or as geographical variants of just one. Nevertheless, they provide the aquarist with interesting fishes with great personality.

References

DARNELL, R. M. (1962) Fishes of the Rio Tamesí and related coastal lagoons in east-central México", *Publ. Inst. Mar. Sci.* 8; pp 299-365.
NIETO, L.M., VELASQUEZ, C., ROJAS, C., AND RIVERA, J. (1984) *Rioverde*. Ayuntamiento de la ciudad de Rioverde.
PELLEGRIN, J. (1903) Description de cichlidés nouveaux de la collection du Muséum. *Bull. Mus. Nat. Paris.* 9; pp 120-125.
TAYLOR, J.N. AND MILLER, R.R. (1983) Cichlid Fishes (Genus *Cichlasoma*) of the Rio Pánuco basin, Eastern México, with description of a new species. *Occ. paper Mus. Nat. His.* Univ. of Kansas. 104; pp 1-24.

"Cichlasoma" minckleyi Kornfield & Taylor, 1983

"Cichlasoma" minckleyi is endemic to the springs at Cuatro Cienegas in the northern part of México, in the state of Coahuila. Cuatro Cienegas lies in the eastern part of the Chihuahua desert. Due to its geographical location it was isolated from other water systems until men built canals to irrigate land and thus connected the springs with the Rio Salado (Rio Grande system).

The water system at Cuatro Cienegas consists of many springs (thermal and cold) that drain into lakes or form small creeks or rivers. The water is very hard, more than 50° DH, and the temperature in a spring I visited in May 1991 was more than 35° C. Originally there were seven independent drainage systems of which most drained into closed lakes (Minckley, 1969). In 1974 only two drainage systems were not interconnected by canals, all others draining into neighbouring systems or into the Rio Salado (La Bounty, 1974). Moreover an extensive underground water system connects several springs with each other and through these underground channels fish may have migrated from one system to another (Minckley, 1969). The basin of Cuatro Cienegas was unchanged for a long period of time, maybe for more than a few million years. Not only cichlids and other fish are endemic to this area but also snails, crustaceans, and reptiles.

"Cichlasoma" minckleyi has received a lot of attention from evolutionary biologists as it is a polymorphic species which could give some clues as to how polymorphism could be associated with the formation of species (Kornfield et al., 1982; Liem & Kaufman, 1984). "C." minckleyi is polymorphic in its shape and in the structure of the pharyngeal teeth. One morph is deep-bodied and has very large, molariform teeth on the pharyngeal bones, whereas another morph has a cylindrical shape and sharp, papilliform pharyngeal teeth (see accompanying photos of at least four different morphs). Several investigations (Sage & Selander, 1975; Kornfield et al., 1982) revealed that other genetic characters, which would indicate that we are dealing with different species, are not coupled to the different morphs. These investigations also proved that the different morphs interbreed resulting in different morphs in one brood. One can thus conclude that, even though the morphs look rather different, they still recognize each other as belonging to one species.

After it became known that the Cuatro Cienegas cichlids represent just one, polymorphic, species and not four different ones (La Bounty, 1974), "C." minckleyi was used in hypotheses as to how (sympatric) speciation in cichlids could take place in general. One theory (Liem & Kaufman, 1984) hypothesises that the different morphs would one day mate assortatively and give rise to new

One of the many springs near Cuatro Cienegas. All photos of "Cichlasoma" minckleyi in this article were taken here.

The elongated morph of *"Cichlasoma" minckleyi*. This specimen was about 18 cm in size.

species. At present, however, all morphs recognize each other as one species and the different morphs seem to feed less specifically than one would expect from their differences in pharyngeal morphology.

Liem & Kaufman (1984) found it unlikely that *"C". minckleyi* originated from hybridisation between two species since the molariform morph is so well developed as to point to a specialisation. But why hybridisation between two species? Couldn't we explain it by the assumption that an early population of *"C." minckleyi* became split up over several springs and adapted itself to the local circumstances? Some of these springs could temporarily have almost dried out and could thus have started a specialisation towards eating snails, an item which was predominantly avoided by the ancestral population. Some other springs could have had a particularly rich population of small fishes on which the local cichlids could have specialised. *"C." minckleyi* seems to be a very variable species; in the almost-dried-out spring the individuals with strong molariform pharyngeal teeth would have an advantage over the generalised morphs, whereas in the fish-rich spring fast swimming individuals would have an advantage. Both these morphs can eat any type of food, as is proven in the laboratory and by field studies, but the highly

specialised molariform morph indicates that there must have been a strong selection for this specialisation. We can hardly explain this highly advanced specialisation by the variability of *"C." minckleyi* alone. A non-assortative mating system, still present today, would have averaged out the genetic characters promoted by the environment.

None of the reports about the Cuatro Cienegas cichlid mentions that, beside the trophic morphs, there are also at least three colour morphs. The most common in the spring I visited in May 1991 was light-blue, the second most common was yellow, and rarely darker, blue-speckled individuals were observed. The yellow and light-blue morphs both had deep-bodied and cylindrically shaped individuals. The darker blue individuals were small (approximately 5 to 10 cm) but seem to have different body shapes as well. Along with this apparently permanent coloration, many very dark coloured individuals were observed. However, when such a dark individual was frightened it quickly changed to its basic color. I have made similar observations for *"C." labridens* in Rio Florido near Cuidad Valles. Although no in depth examination was made, it seemed that only elongated individuals of *"C." minckleyi* turned black and that they did so when hunting (small fish?).

If we combine the variability in trophic characters

A deep-bodied, light-blue morph "C." minckleyi.

The hunting(?) colour is fading in this yellow individual.

A deep-bodied, yellow morph "C." minkleyi.

An intermediate morph "C." minckleyi.

with the presence of different colour morphs then we are likely to conclude that these characters have developed independently in isolated populations. There they could have evolved into highly advanced forms without the averaging effect of interbreeding. Only after these isolated or even semi-isolated populations had evolved into geographical variants, adapted to their specific environment, were they united by the building of canals connecting the once isolated springs. Speciation had not advanced far enough to abolish species recognition among the different populations and thus interbreeding produced the variable population as we know it today.

References

KORNFIELD, I.L., SMITH, D.C., GAGNON, P.S., & TAYLOR, J.N. (1982) The cichlid fish of Cuatro Cienegas, Mexico: Direct evidence of conspecificity among distinct morphs. *Evolution* 36, pp. 658-664.
LA BOUNTY, J.F. (1974) Materials for the revision of cichlids from northern Mexico and southern Texas, U.S.A. PhD. thesis. Arizona State Univ.
LIEM, K.F. & KAUFMAN, L.S. (1984) Intraspecific macroevolution: functional biology of the polymorphic cichlid species *Cichlasoma minkleyi*. in: *Evolution of Fish Species Flocks* (eds. A.A. Echelle and I. Kornfield). University of Maine at Orono Press, Orono, Maine, pp. 203-215.
MINCKLEY, W.L. (1969) Environments of the bolson of Cuatro Cienegas, Coahuila, Mexico, with special reference to the aquatic biota. *Texas Western Press*, Univ. Texas, El Paso, Sci. Ser. 2; pp. 1-63.
SAGE, R.D. & SELANDER, R.K. (1975) Trophic radiation through polymorphism in cichlid fishes. *Proc. Nat. Acad. Sci. USA*. Vol. 72, No. 11, pp 4669-4673.

"Cichlasoma" septemfasciatum Regan, 1908

Willem Heijns

The female of the Topaz Cichlid, *"Cichlasoma" septemfasciatum*, shows a brighter coloration than the male.

Shortly after the creation of Central America by tectonic activity the narrow stretch of new land was completely devoid of a freshwater fish fauna. But, as might be expected, this situation didn't continue for long. A great colonisation spread from the south to occupy the newly created land. Cichlids probably played an important role as they were among the fishes able to migrate via the sea.

How exactly the colonisation took place remains unknown, but the populations of fish entering the new land found themselves confronted with a continental divide, and they could colonize either the Pacific or the Atlantic drainage. Once settled they could not cross the divide, which acted as a barrier that kept the populations on either side isolated. Populations derived from one original species could thus develop independently, sometimes into new species.

This mechanism has led to the evolution of a number of sibling species, especially in the southern part of Central America. One example is by *"Cichlasoma" sajica* and *"C." septemfasciatum*, where the first is restricted to the Pacific and the second to the Atlantic drainage.

"C." septemfasciatum is distributed over a much larger area than *"C." sajica*. This has resulted in several populations which differ mainly in coloration. Many colour variants of *"C." septemfasciatum* are thus known. An overview of these races can be found in *"Buntbarsche der neuen Welt: Mittelamerika"* by Werner and Stawikowski.

A new population of this species was discovered in 1986 in the Rio Sixaola, in the south of Costa Rica near the border with Panama. This race of *"C." septemfasciatum* became known as the Topaz Cichlid. It is characterized by a vibrant yellow-orange coloration which is also visible in males. Initial reports on this cichlid mentioned that a formal description was on its way but this has never materialized.

A male of the Topaz Cichlid. Photo by Willem Heijns.

Theraps * *coeruleus* Stawikowski & Werner, 1987

Willem Heijns

The female *Theraps coeruleus* is characterized by the blue spot in the dorsal fin. Photos by Willem Heijns.

In 1985, Stawikowski and Werner discovered a small cichlid which they named "Small Blue" (Kleine Blaue) and brought it back alive to Germany. In the same year, after the authors had published a report about their new discovery, Seeger and Staeck described *Theraps rheophilus* and remarked that the newly discovered cichlid of Stawikowski and Werner could be a variant of their species. The "Small Blue" indeed resembled the specimens which were depicted in the description of *T. rheophilus*. Later it became clear that Seegers and Staeck had been mistaken and *T. rheophilus* was designated a junior synonym of *T. lentiginosus*. In 1987 Stawikowski and Werner described *T. coeruleus*.

The type locality of *T. coeruleus* lies 30 km south of Palenque in the Rio Mizol Há, México. The river is a tributary of the Rio Tulija which, in its turn, is an affluent of the Rio Grijalva.

In the description of *T. coeruleus* Stawikowski and Werner provide some characteristics by which the genus *Theraps* can be distinguished from other cichlasomini. This forms a basis on which cichlids that comply with these characteristics can be placed in the genus. The type species of the genus is *T. irregularis*. Other species belonging to the genus are *T. lentiginosus* and *T. coeruleus*.

All three species are rheophilic, i.e. they inhabit fast flowing water. This also could be the reason why *T. coeruleus* was not been discovered earlier. One does not expect to find cichlids in the middle of fast flowing streams, and when one does they prove to be difficult to catch.

T. coeruleus feeds on insect larvae which are found among the pebbles on the bottom of the stream. Such small stones are turned over and the prey secured by a quick bite, preventing it from being carried away by the stream. This behaviour is also observed in the aquarium. Apart from the crystal clear water they demand, *T. coeruleus* is an easy to maintain and very attractive cichlid.

* (We are not certain whether the generic status of *Theraps* is fully accepted. The name is used tentatively. *MB*.)

The blue spot lacks in the male *T. coeruleus*.

Thorichthys pasionis (Rivas, 1962)

Willem Heijns

A male *Thorichthys pasionis*. Photo by Willem Heijns.

Since the revision of the genus *Cichlasoma* by Kullander (1983) the nomen *Thorichthys* has become more and more current, in scientific as well as in aquaristic literature, for species which formed that section within the original large genus. The genus *Thorichthys* comprises not more than eight species, five of which form a natural sub-group. *T. aureus* is the best known of this group. The other three form a natural group as well, of which the Firemouth Cichlid, *T. meeki*, enjoys great popularity among aquarists. The other two species of this sub-group are *T. affinis* and *T. pasionis*. The two sub-groups differ in the shape of the mouth. The lower jaw of *T. pasionis* and sister species protrudes slightly further than the upper (prognathous) whereas the jaws in the species of the other sub-group are equally long (isognathous). The feeding technique of both groups may therefore differ as well; the prognathous species may scoop their food from the substrate whereas the isognathous cichlids pick their choice out of the sediment. However, nothing factual is known about their natural feeding behavior.

T. meeki is the best known species of the genus. *T. pasionis* is closely related to this cichlid and the only difference, besides its distribution, is its yellow coloration. This has led to its trade name of Yellow Meeki. Indeed, *T. pasionis* closely resembles the two other species of the sub-group. The basic coloration of the body is violet-blue; the head and lower part of the body show many yellow areas. The most prominent characteristic, however, is the colour of the throat: dark bordeaux-red to almost black. The colour of the throat in *T. meeki* is red and in *T. affinis* is yellow. Specimens of *T. pasionis* in breeding coloration have a black throat. Normally the colour on the throat is not visible, but this makes its effect more dramatic when the fish lowers the buccal cavity in a threatening display. The sharp contrast the suddenly appearing black throat forms with the yellow colour on the head must act as an effective means to deter intruders.

T. pasionis is found in the Rio Usumacinta drainage (Rio de la Pasion) and in the Lago Petén Itzá in Guatemala and southern part of Mexico.

T. pasionis is found in streams as well as in lakes. It forages over sometimes muddy bottoms searching for small prey such as insect larvae and crustaceans.

In contrast to some other species of the genus, *T. pasionis* is relatively easy to keep in an aquarium. They quickly adjust to the conditions of the aquarium and take any type of food offered. The only requirement they have is for clean, oxygen-rich water.

SOUTH AMERICAN CICHLIDS

Crenicichla species from the Rio Xingú

Frank Warzel

For many, the Rio Xingú is a shallow 2000 km-long tributary of the Amazonas which is, by virtue of its many rapids, inaccessible to larger boats. For ichthyologists and interested aquarists the Rio Xingú is the supplier of an inexhaustible array of unusual tetras, catfish, and cichlids. Recent investigations have indicated that most fishes in the Rio Xingú system are endemic to these waters. A large part of the fauna still awaits a scientific description although publications concerning the region's fish-fauna have increased recently. On the other hand it seems that many species, which have already been imported for aquaristic purposes, are absent from museum collections. This will certainly hamper their description in the near future.

In the group of nameless cichlids we find several *Crenicichla* species of which the first was collected in 1988 near Altamira by Schliewen, Stawikowski, and Kilian. A few weeks after its discovery juveniles of this cichlid, introduced as *Crenicichla* sp. "Xingú", were exported from Belém.

At the same location a year earlier, in the summer of 1987, Bergleiter hooked two large *Crenicichla* species that appeared to be unknown to science. Reports that a pitch-black *Crenicichla*

A female *Crenicichla* sp. "Xingú III" with typical coloration (TL approx. 20 cm). Photos by Frank Warzel.

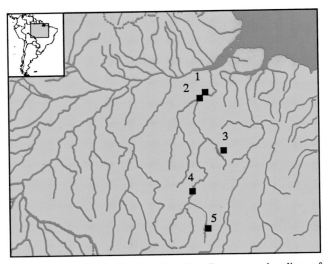

1. Altamira; 2. Cachoeira do Espelho, type locality of C. percna; 3. Rio Fresco, type locality of C. phaiospilus; 4. Cachoeira von Martius, collecting site of C. phaiospilus; 5. Suiá Missú, collection site of C. sp. "Suiá Missú".

Crenicichla sp. "Xingú I", juveniles (TL c. 15 cm).

Crenicichla sp. "Xingú I", adult male.

Crenicichla sp. "Xingú I", female in breeding coloration.

was observed near rocks and in large caves (Schliewen, pers. comm.) indicated that at least two species were present. Further imports from Altamira proved that not one but two other species were to be found there. These latter two were named C. sp. "Xingú II" and C. sp. "Xingú III" (Warzel, 1990a).

A fourth species from Altamira was exported in September 1990 and introduced as C. sp. "Xingú IV" (Warzel, 1990b). In the meantime this species has been scientifically described as C. percna Kullander, 1991. C. phaiospilus is known to occur in the Rio Xingú but has not yet been exported alive. A sixth species was discovered by Harald Schultz in the Suiá Missú, a tributary of the Rio Xingú.

It is likely that most (if not all) of these six *Crenicichla* species are endemic to the Xingú system. One of the indicators of their supposed endemism is their relatively high developed specialization. C. sp. "Xingú I", for instance, was observed only in shallow, fast-flowing sections of the river. It has a very slender body and in the aquarium it swims in a peculiar oblique position. In contrast, C. sp. "Xingú III" has a, for *Crenicichla*, compressed body with a relatively large head and eyes. Observations of this species in the wild and also in part in the aquarium indicate that it prefers caves or dark recesses. C. percna, a species with an extremely shallow head and snout, is also highly specialized. Although reports about observations in its natural environment have not been published, aquarium observations suggest that we are dealing with a bottom-oriented ambush hunter. I have observed that C. percna sometimes rests itself on a rock or on the bottom of the aquarium, almost feigning to be dead. The usually light-brown spots on its body then become very dark and form a conspicuous pattern. Such interesting behaviour was frequently practised when smaller fishes could be seen by C. percna.

The specialization, if any, of C. sp. "Xingú II" and C. phaiospilus is at present unknown. Both species have a shallow pointed head and high-positioned eyes.

C. sp. "Suiá Missú" from the upper Xingú has a "normal" shape and is the only species of the six to have a head profile which resembles those of C. johanna, C. strigata, and C. lenticulata. Adults of latter species have a rather rounded snout. In contrast to the other five species, C. sp. "Suiá Missú" was not found in the vicinity of rapids or fast flowing water. Lowe-McConnell (1991) found this species in a small lake-like widening of a stream near Córrego do Gato.

C. sp. "Suiá Missú" has a characteristic colour

pattern which is different from all other *Crenicichla*. The ground colour is grey-green with round, black spots in the dorsal portion of the body. These spots are bigger and merge together towards the end of the body. Only males seem to have spotted dorsal fins. The red spots in the spinous part of the dorsal fin are unique in *Crenicichla*.

C. percna and *C. phaiospilus* also show a peculiar colour pattern. *C. percna* (Gr. perknos = dark spotted) has a leopard pattern with three or four black spots on its flanks whereas *C. phaiospilus* (Gr. phaios = dark, spilus = spot) shows four to five black blotches on the side.

The pitch-black coloration of *C.* sp. "Xingú III" is also uncommon. Only one other species in this genus is known to have such a coloration, namely *C. cametana* Steindachner, 1911 from the Araguaia and the Rio Tocantíns which are not far from the Rio Xingú. This does not automatical-ly mean that both species are closely related. *C. percna, C. phaiospilus*, and *C.* sp. "Suiá Missú" lack the normally present light-bordered spots at the base of the caudal peduncle.

The colour patterns of *C.* sp. "Xingú I" and *C.* sp. "Xingú II" fall in the normal range of *Crenicichla*, although both have exceptionally intensive red hues, especially in the unpaired fins. Rarely, and then only in excited emotional phases, a zebra-like colour pattern is seen on *C.* sp. "Xingú I" consising of about 9 to 10 thin, vertical bars which reach halfway to the ventral region of the body. Out of all the Xingú species, it is mainly juveniles of the latter species that have been imported. They have an intense orange-yellow ground colour with a pattern of horizontal stripes which remain to a size of about 20 cm. Such a juvenile pattern is also known for other species in this group. As long as these cichlids have this pattern, their behaviour is rather peaceful and they show a tendency to form schools. It is somewhat more difficult to mix *C.* sp. "Xingú II" and *C.* sp. "Xingú III" with other fish. In particular juveniles of *C.* sp. "Xingú III" are pugnacious towards conspecifics and become solitary at an early age. Specimens of *C.* sp. "Xingú II" first start to change their colour pattern at a size of 10 cm. *C.* sp. "Xingú III" juveniles, however, at

Crenicichla sp "Xingú I", adult female.

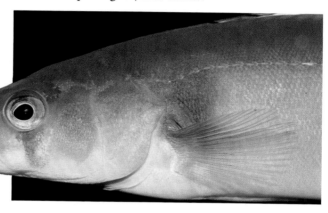

Crenicichla sp "Xingú II", adult female.

Crenicichla sp "Xingú III", adult female.

Crenicichla percna, adult. Photos by Frank Warzel.

Crenicichla sp. "Xingú II", juvenile (c. 12 cm TL).

Crenicichla sp. "Xingú II", female in breeding coloration.

this size have a completely dark pattern and are indistinguishable from large adults. Even the typical iris-crescent behind the pupil is obvious in small specimens.

Although it may seem like that these six species have a rather distinct appearance and behaviour, they all have morphometric characters in common which place them in a group apart from other *Crenicichla*.

If one is considering maintaining one or several of these pike cichlids in the aquarium, attention should be paid to the individual sizes of these fish. Most grow to a length of more than 30 cm, with the possible exception of *C. percna*, and therefore need a large, at least 200 cm long, aquarium. In addition, these pikes grow enormously fast and juveniles of 10 cm may add 15 cm in the first year after importation. Large tanks with plenty of swimming space are a must, especially for *C.* sp. "Xingú I". The chemical composition of the water seems to be of minor importance in so far as the well-being of these cichlids is concerned. Owing to the fast turn-over of food, frequent water changes are necessary and should keep the build-up of nitrates to a minimum.

Until now none of the Xingú species has been spawned in the aquarium. An analysis of the water near Altamira (Schliewen & Stawikowski,

Crenicichla phaiospilus (above) and *Crenicichla* sp. "Suiá Missú" (below). Drawings by Frank Warzel.

1989) showed (September, 1988) a temperature of 32.2° C, a pH of 6.5, a hardness of circa 1° DH and a conductivity of 120 μS/cm. Even under perfectly imitated water conditions, a spawning could not be induced. Under these circumstances, however, the females showed their breeding coloration and had ripe ovaries. Females of *C.* sp. "Xingú I" attracted males by approaching them in a bent, U-shaped position of the body, with the central part of the body became very light and conspicuous at the same time. It is known from other *Crenicichla* that females bend their bodies in an S-shape during the courtship ritual.

Hopefully more specimens will be exported in near future, so that we may increase our knowledge of the behaviour and distribution of these impressive and beautiful pike cichlids.

References

KULLANDER, S.O. (1991) *Crenicichla phaiospilus* and *C. percna*, two new species of pike cichlids (Teleostei: Cichlidae) from the Rio Xingú, Brazil. *Ichthyol. Explor. Freshwaters.*Vol. 1, (4), pp 351-360.
LOWE-McCONNELL, R.H. (1991) Natural history of fishes in Araguaia and Xingu Amazonian tributaries, Serra do Roncador, Mato Grosso, Brazil. *Ichthyol. Explor. Freshwaters.*Vol. 2 (1), pp 63-82.
SCHLIEWEN, U & STAWIKOWSKI, R. (1989) *Teleocichla. DATZ* (42) 8; pp 227-231.
WARZEL, F. (1989) Neu importiert: *Crenicichla* aus Brasilien. *DATZ* (42) 8; pp 456-457
WARZEL, F. (1990a) Neu importiert: *Crenicichla* aus dem nördlichen Brasilien (II). *DATZ* (43) 12; pp 713-714.
WARZEL, F. (1990b) Neu importiert: *Crenicichla* spec. "Xingú IV". *DATZ* (44) 1; p 7.

Crenicichla percna, an adult specimen of unknown sex from Altamira. Photos by Frank Warzel.

Crenicichla sp. cf. *regani*

Frank Warzel

A female *Crenicichla* sp. cf. *regani* from the Rio Xingú near Altamira, Brazil, in breeding coloration. Photos by Frank Warzel.

A male *Crenicichla* sp. cf. *regani*.

Before I report on *Crenicichla* sp. cf. *regani*, another, closely related, dwarf Pike Cichlid −*C. regani*− should be mentioned. This attractive small *Crenicichla* was exported in the early seventies and became known under trade names like "Nanus" or "Dorsocellata". *Crenicichla regani* was described by Ploeg (1989) from a large collection of specimens. This dwarf Pike Cichlid seems to have a wide distribution in Amazonia. Ploeg presumed that *C. regani* was not present in the Rio Negro and that here its niche would be occupied by *C. notophthalmus*. Windisch (pers. comm.), however, found dwarf Pikes in the Rio Negro (together with *C. notophthalmus*) which

showed a close resemblance to *C. regani*. Underwater photographs, taken by Bergleiter (pers. comm.) in the lower Rio Xingú near Souzel, showed *C. regani* in its natural habitat.

The dwarf Pike depicted in the photographs, *Crenicichla* sp. cf. *regani*, was collected by Rainer Harnoss in a small ditch near Altamira, Rio Xingú drainage, Brazil, about 200 km upstream from Souzel. This cichlid differs from *C. regani* in having a smaller adult size, a shorter snout, a deeper body, and conspicuous markings in the tail. The maximum size of *C.* sp. cf. *regani* seems to be about 6 cm for males and 4.5 cm for females.

At a length of 4 cm the female assumed breeding coloration. Instead of courting her "own" partner she showed off, with her body bent in the typical S-position and fins erect, to a much larger male *C. regani* in an adjacent aquarium. Unfortunately the female ignored her partner during the entire period during which it seemed that she was willing to spawn. After about six weeks she lost her beautiful coloration, which is common for *Crenicichla*. Unusually the conspicuous black and white marking in the dorsal fin disappeared as well. This phenomenon is known only from Pike Cichlids of the *C. lugubris* complex; they too can "switch off" the coloration in the dorsal fin when they stop breeding.

Acaronia vultuosa Kullander, 1989

Frank Warzel

Acaronia vultuosa from the Rio Atabapo, Colombia. Photo by Frank Warzel.

Bocca de juquiá (giant-mouthed fish); this is the name Brazilian fishermen gave cichlids of the genus *Acaronia*. They gained this name because of their large, oblique mouth with which they are able to suck in sometimes rather large sized prey at an astonishing speed.

Besides *Acaronia nassa*, the newly described *A. vultuosa* has also been infrequently imported as an aquarium fish. Both species are identified by their characteristic markings on the head. *A. vultuosa* has a very conspicuous pattern consisting of several lines. The pattern in *A. nassa* has broader bands and round spots which in part have a light edge. The two species, which show a great resemblance towards each other, have a mostly allopatric distribution and are regarded as sibling species. *A. nassa* is found in the Amazonas drainage while *A. vultuosa* lives in the Orinoco system. Only in the upper Rio Negro have both species been found sympatrically. This is probably caused by the Casiquiare which forms a connection between the two river systems.

In Spring 1991 we found *A. vultuosa* in the Rio Atabapo, south of the Casiquiare. Its biotope, however, was not in the river itself but about 100 m from the bank in a lagoon fed with water from a spring. We found many *A. vultuosa* in different stages of growth mainly at the heavily vegetated edge of the lagoon. Habitat descriptions in the literature confirm that *A. vultuosa* prefers stagnant or slowly flowing water. Its preference for this type of water is further indicated by its typical swimming behaviour: it swims in short bursts, stopping suddenly while scanning the area for possible prey. Normally, however, *A. vultuosa* hovers among the weeds and ambushes its prey.

Although *Acaronia* lives in soft, acidic water, it accepts regular tap water without any signs of distress. It takes any type of frozen food but ignores flakes or pelleted aquarium fare. *A. vultuosa* is not a cichlid for a regular community aquarium. It can show many defensive and threatening postures but in general it behaves a little shyly towards other fishes, even towards cichlids that are noticeably smaller.

A. vultuosa remains smaller than *A. nassa*; the biggest specimen recorded measured about 18 cm. The largest specimens we collected in the Rio Atabapo were still a few centimetres short of this length.

Further observations concerning the behaviour of this cichlid have not yet been published. One of these days I will dim the lights of the tank in order to find out the reason for its large eyes.

Guianacara sp. "Red Cheek"

Ron Bernhard

A pair of *Guianacara* sp. "Red Cheek" from Venezuela. Photo by Ron Bernhard.

In 1902, the French ichthyologist Pellegrin described the cichlid *Acara geayi* in honour of the collector F. Geay, who caught a number of specimens in the Rio Camopi in French Guiana. Later the species was placed in the genus *Aequidens* and until 1989 it was known as *A. geayi* (Pellegrin, 1902).

The popularity of this cichlid among aquarists spawned a vast amount of publications which made the name *Aequidens geayi* well-known among hobbyists.

The Swedish ichthyologist Sven Kullander is known for two reasons. Firstly for his meticulous morphological examinations of South American cichlids and secondly for his ability to produce an infinite number of descriptions of species and genera. As early as in 1980 he indicated his doubts about the placement of *geayi* in *Aequidens* and pointed to the relationship this cichlid has with those of the genus *Acarichthys*. Nine years later Kullander not only introduced a new genus but also two subgenera and three new species! The genus *Guianacara* and subgenera *Guianacara* and *Oelemaria* are described in *"The Cichlids of Surinam"* co-authored by Han Nijssen. The species *G. geayi*, *G. owroewefi* and *G. sphenozona* belong to the subgenus *Guianacara*, whereas the subgenus *Oelemaria* contains only *G. oelemariensis*.

The cichlid which is depicted in the photograph above resembles *G. owroewefi* in many characteristics. The main feature of this species is the black spot on the anterior part of the dorsal fin and a black vertical stripe which is most intensively coloured on and just below the upper lateral line.

Seen from a geographical standpoint the "Red Cheek Geayi" is unlikely to be conspecific with *G. owroewefi*, as it is found in Venezuela whereas *G. owroewefi* is distributed over central and east Surinam. These two populations are separated by that of *G. sphenozona* which inhabits the river systems (mainly the Corantijn River) in the western part of Surinam.

G. oelemariensis seems to be endemic in the Oelemari River where it is sympatric with *G. owroewefi*. Without doubt the "Red Cheek Geayi" belongs to the subgenus *Guianacara* and will be referred to as *Guianacara* sp. "Red Cheek".

The "Red Cheek Geayi" is one of the most beautiful species of this genus. Its maximum length is about 14 cm for males and about 10 cm for females. It has been bred in captivity where it proved to be a cave spawner. The female may disappear into the cave for the entire period during which the eggs develop into free swimming fry. The pair bond is strong and they continue to defend their territory when no fry are present.

Krobia species

Ron Bernhard

The red-eyed *Krobia* species was collected in French Guiana. Photos by Ron Bernhard.

Krobia sp. "Green", a female fanning her eggs.

A male *Krobia guianensis*.

Before Kullander's revision in 1989 the genus *Aequidens* contained many South American cichlids which could be placed in several groups. Then Kullander placed the species which were considered as the *guianensis*-group in the new genus *Krobia*. The best-known species of the former group was known to aquarists by the name *itanyi*, but later it turned out to be *guianensis*. These two species, now *Krobia guianensis* and *K. itanyi*, differ from each other only in their breeding pigmentation patterns. The pattern of *K. guianensis* changes during breeding to vertical bars on the body whereas that of *K. itanyi* remains a horizontal stripe.

When Kullander (1989) defined the new genus he mentioned that besides the two described species in *Krobia* there were two others known to occur in French Guiana. In the aquarium hobby two undescribed species of this genus are known, of which one, *Krobia* sp. "Red Eye" was collected in French Guiana. The other species, *K.* sp. "Green" came from an unknown location and has already disappeared from the aquaristic scene. *Krobia* species are open substrate spawners. The eggs are always laid on the same spot in the territory, which is defended by the pair, even when no fry are present. The pair bond is strong and remains for years.

The "Aufwuchs-feeder"

Roger Häggström

When it comes to the mbuna of Lake Malawi, it is well known that they spend most of their time feeding from the Aufwuchs on the surface of rocks. In a normal community aquarium, though, the fish don't spend much time feeding this way. They don't spend much time feeding in any way. Ever since I have been keeping mbuna, I have wanted to give them the chance to feed in a natural way. The result of my deliberations is the "Aufwuchs-feeder" which I describe below.

This simple device consists of a PVC tube, a square of plastic gauze, rubber bands, four plastic bars, and four rust-free screws. The idea is to put the food between the tube (rock equivalent) and the gauze so that the fish have to scrape the food through the gauze in order to eat.

A PVC tube (20 cm long and with a diameter of 10 cm) is cut lengthwise into two halves which can be used for two "Aufwuchs-feeders". Drill a hole in one end (the "top") of the half-tube and tie a plastic string in this hole. The string should be as long as your tank's height plus 10 cm. Tie a handle of plastic or wood at the other end of the string. This handle should hang over the rim of the aquarium thus making it easy to remove the feeder from the tank.

The plastic gauze (18 x 15 cm) can be purchased in some hardware stores. It is used as insect-screen. It should be a little stiff for easy maintenance. The mesh should not be more than 2 mm. Brass or stainless steel screens work as well. Cut four bars out of a sheet of PVC with the sizes 20 x 1 cm and about 2 mm thick. Glue (PVC glue) the plastic net between two bars on each side of the long end (see photo). These bars will pull the gauze tight over the half-tube. A hole is drilled in each end of both plastic (double) bars. The four screws are mounted in these holes (see photo). On one side a rubber band is tied to each screw.

Now you can load the feeder. Use whatever food is available as long as it is not too hard or soluble in the water. Pelleted food or frozen food is placed on the net and rolled flat using the half-tube. Then take the loose ends of the rubber bands, draw them round the tube and mount them on the screws on the other end of the net. Rinse the whole feeder in running water and put it in the aquarium.

At first it will take some time before the fish discover the food, but then you can watch them feeding in their natural way. This may promote the growth of the lips of cichlids like *Placidochromis milomo* or *Protomelas ornatus*. Now it takes much longer before all food has been eaten.

I think this device could be regarded as the equivalent of the wheel in a hamster cage.

The "Aufwuchs-feeder" let the cichlids eat in a natural way and prolongs the feeding period.

Breeding *Tropheus* the natural way

Gerard Tijsseling

Tropheus moorii is one of the favourite cichlids from Lake Tanganyika. It has been bred in captivity by thousands of aquarists. Some of them practise early removal of larvae from the female's mouth in order to have a higher survival rate of the entire spawn.

Among organisms like birds and animals, nature has provided a process whereby the newly-born individual learns some important "tricks" from its mother which help it to survive, and which can play an important role at a later stage of its life, e.g. when choosing a partner. This process is called imprinting and usually takes place a few hours or days after birth.

In my opinion fry of *T. moorii* and similar mouth-brooders from Lake Tanganyika are also imprinted during the first few hours after they have been released from the female's mouth. In my experience, young which had been taken out of the mouth at a premature stage grew up to be bad mouthbrooding females that swallowed or neglected the first three to five spawns. Young which had been released naturally, grew up to be excellent females that brooded the first spawn to maturity.

In a community aquarium it is hardly possible to let females release their babies naturally; in most cases the fry will be eaten in minutes. Therefore I thought of imitating the situation in the lake where fry are released in the extreme shallows. These areas have many advantages: they are inaccessible to larger fish (predators) and have plenty of food. Algae-eaters find most of their food in the shallows as these are the lightest areas. Small rocks and pebbles provide a substrate for the algae and the necessary shelter.

The photograph shows how a "shallows" can be built onto your tank. Among my friends this set-up is known as "tank with balcony". The platform is glued to one of the tank's sides. The "balcony" in the photograph has a size of 70 x 50 cm. In my experience 15 cm is the maximum depth for such a platform because deeper "balconies" will be occupied by territorial males.

The "balcony" is filled with small stones. Care must be taken to provide oxygen-rich water (place water inlet over the platform) and lots of light (to stimulate algae growth).

The best thing is: it works perfectly! When a female is about to release her fry she swims up to the "balcony" and stays a week or more with her offspring before she returns to the group in the rest of the tank. The young, however, stay on the "balcony" till they have reached a size of about two centimetres.

Not only *Tropheus* but also Goby cichlids (Eretmodini) use the "balcony" with success.

The platform is glued to one of the tank's sides. Photo by Gerard Tijsseling.

The cichlid bible

Martin Geerts

About twenty years ago C. M. Yonge (in his foreword to Fryer & Iles, *The cichlid fishes of the Great Lakes of Africa*, 1972) described the Great Lakes in East Africa as "a field laboratory of evolution". Although Yonge is a malacologist (mollusc-expert) and Lake Tanganyika harbours a great variety of snails, we may assume that he was thinking of the cichlid species flocks when he put these words on paper. The East African cichlids have since then been in the limelight of aquarists, ichthyologists and evolutionary biologists. A few years later Dr. P. H. Greenwood (1974, Cichlid fishes of Lake Victoria, East Africa) remarked that the increased attention given to these cichlids had negatively influenced the studies of other African freshwater fishes and even of neotropical cichlids.

The present situation does not seem to be much different from then as we read in *"Cichlid Fishes; Behaviour, Ecology and Evolution"*. This book, "the cichlid bible", was published recently by Chapman & Hall (London). The text is a compilation of papers by almost twenty authors, all authorities in their field, edited by Miles Keenleyside. The result of their efforts is a must for every "cichlidologist" as it contains all the knowledge concerning cichlids gathered in the last decades. Curiously, this knowledge is not reflected in handbooks about evolution.

The first chapter of the "bible" treats the intrafamilial relationships of cichlids and is written by Melanie Stiassny. Interestingly, given Greenwood's remarks, Stiassny places the cichlids of the East African lakes in a group called "The Rest". The lamprologine cichlids are an exception but during a congress held in The Hague (28-8-1991) she expressed her doubts as to the correct place this group has in her cladogram.

That not everything in the "field laboratory of evolution" has its proper place may be illustrated by the fact that Ribbink (Chapter 2: 38) regards the mbuna as a monophyletic group, while Kornfield (Chapter 5: 121) speaks of "....as currently defined, the Mbuna is a paraphyletic group". Tony Ribbink treats the ecology of the cichlids in Africa's Great Lakes with authority, even though the emphasis is put on Malawian cichlids. Yamaoka, in his treatment of the "Feeding relationships" (Chapter 7), restores the imbalance by referring mainly to Tanganyikan cichlids. Yamaoka's contribution is of great interest especially the paragraph titled "How to coexist?". This paragraph also makes clear that much research is still needed to elucidate the way East African cichlids influence each others life styles. Furthermore Yamaoka discusses the techniques with which East African cichlids exploit different sources of food.

Cichlids have a well adapted feeding apparatus and this aspect is discussed by Karl Liem in a separate chapter. Liem's contribution describes the functional morphology of cichlids. Trophic radiation is commonly regarded as the main cause of success in cichlids, which is clearly why Liem puts emphasis on the technique with which cichlids collect and process food. His final words, however, show the great need of additional research: "In short, comparative functional morphology has demonstrated the shortcomings of our current and generally favoured interpretations of cichlid diversifications, as monophyletic in origin and driven by competition in faunistically closed basins."

In general biology the species concept is still a hot point of discussion. Greenwood's chapter concerning this issue is therefore of great interest. With regard to recent investigations on *"Cichlasoma" managuense*, he points to the necessity of making a distinction between ecophenotypic variation and polymorphism. On page 93 Greenwood expresses his disbelief that the presence of predators, like the Nile perch or the tigerfish, would hamper speciation. Even the catastrophy in Lake Victoria, caused by the introduction of the Nile perch, could not change his opinion.

The impact the Nile perch had on the species flock in Lake Victoria is further discussed by Barel, Ligtvoet, Goldschmidt, Witte, and Goudswaard. The authors do not restrict themselves to a description of this ecological disaster but give information about species identification, ecology, and morphology as well. From a taxonomic point of view the cichlids from Lake Victoria seem to provide a so far unsolvable problem, even at the generic level. This situation is also reflected in the treatment of the genus *Haplochromis* in the recently published *Check-List of the Freshwater Fishes of Africa* (CLOFFA) (part IV). In this checklist Greenwood's revisions of the genus are not accepted. According to Barel *et al.* species identification is a fundamental problem for which modern taxonomic procedures offer no solution (p. 268). The authors find differences in colour patterns among haplochromines that are morphologically identical. Sexual selection, therefore, could provide for a necessary reproductive isolation.

Mating systems and sexual selection are treated in separate chapters. George Barlow discusses mating systems among cichlids. He believes that the evolution of mating systems proceeded from monogamy with biparental care (substrate-guarding species) to polygamy with maternal care (mouthbrooding species). Barlow comments on many aspects of the different breeding techniques and does so with authority. Neverthless a few mistakes have slipped into this chapter. *Tilapia rendalli* is not a biparental mouthbrooder as is stated on p. 180. This species is a substrate spawner and that puts the words of Barlow in a different perspective. On the same page *Tilapia mariae* is treated as a mouthbrooder. *Aequidens vittatus* (= *Bujurquina vittata*) is not found in Surinam. According to Kullander & Nijssen (*The Cichlids of Surinam*) Barlow's reference relates to *Krobia guianensis*. Barlow's remarks concerning the effects of predation make it clear that fry and juveniles run the greatest risk of being eaten. Parental care is therefore of utmost importance and is treated by Keenleyside (Chapter 9). The author reviews investigations which have been performed in the field and this makes his contribution of great value to hobbyists.

Spawning and guarding of fry demand a coordination between the parents. Mark Nelissen discusses communication between cichlids. He distinguishes several forms of communication.

The importance of communication is considered in the chapter written by David Noakes, which deals with the ontogeny of cichlid behavior.

Kenneth McKaye comments on sexual selection (Chapter 12). Sexual selection is currently regarded as the prime factor in speciation among cichlids. McKaye questions whether even the nest building of certain populations of sand-dwelling cichlids could lead to speciation. He writes "Hence we conclude that bower (= nest. *Ed.*) form evolves primarily in response to female choice." Ad Konings (pers. comm.) does not believe so. In his opinion the way a nest is built is mainly dependent on the depth at which it is made. At deeper levels the females see the nests from above which makes the height less important.

Rosemary Lowe-McConnell describes the distribution and ecology of South American and African riverine cichlids. She gives us an authorative overview of the situation.

The last chapter concerns the breeding of cichlids for food and is written by R. Pullin.

"Cichlid Fishes; Behaviour, Ecology and Evolution", the bible, is indispensable for every "cichlidologist". From the text in the book it is apparent that about 50% of the species in "the field laboratory of evolution" await formal description, while many genera are in need of a better diagnosis. Moreover nothing is known about the relationships between many different groups of species. This may be the reason why cichlids, a prime example of speciation, are so poorly represented in books about evolution.

The nest of *Cyathopharynx furcifer*, here the variant in Moliro Bay, varies in height according to the depth at which it is built.

Cichlid classics

Mary Bailey

Recent years have seen several major revisions of cichlid genera, with, in most cases, the original genus being restricted to a few of its former species, and new genera being erected for the remainder. Frequently the gender of the new generic names has differed from that of the original genus, necessitating alterations to some of the specific names as well. As Latin is no longer generally taught in schools the average aquarist has been left in a state of some confusion, and it is hoped that this article will cast a little light upon the subject.

The language of taxonomy is nominally Latin, but many of the word used are latinised forms of words from other languages (mainly Greek) and proper names from all over the world. The grammar of taxonomy is, however, strictly Latin.

Under the trinomial system of nomenclature, devised by Linnaeus in the 18th century, all living beings are classified by three names (the meaning of trinominal): the generic, the specific, and the sub-specific. All generic names are nouns (words which name a thing); "fish" is a noun which tells us with what part of the animal kingdom we are dealing, and likewise *Tropheus, Etroplus, Aequidens*, are Latin nouns, generic names which specify particular groups of fish species.

Latin nouns all have a gender —masculine, feminine, or neuter— which, in classical Latin, is usually recognisable by the ending of the word. The best known are "-us" (masculine), "-a" (feminine), and "-um" (neuter). Unfortunately in taxonomy it is not quite that simple, as if a generic name is a latinised form of a word from another language, it retains its original gender (if any). Thus *Cichlasoma*, which has Greek "roots", appears feminine at first glance because of its "a" ending, but is in fact neuter. It may be necessary to refer back to the original generic description in order to establish the derivation, and hence the gender, of a generic name. Aquarists who find themselves confused may take heart from the fact that even the greatest taxonomists can themselves sometimes be in error —the Greek word "gramma" can mean "letter", in which case it is neuter, or "line", when it is feminine; Dr. C. T. Regan confused the genders of the two when erecting *Apistogramma*, and, while meaning "line", used the neuter gender. This error remained uncorrected until Kullander (1980) revised the genus.

If we wish to refer to a particular member of a genus then we must use the specific name, eg *Tropheus duboisi*. The specific name "qualifies" the generic; "duboisi" tells us that we are dealing with a particular type of *Tropheus*, that named

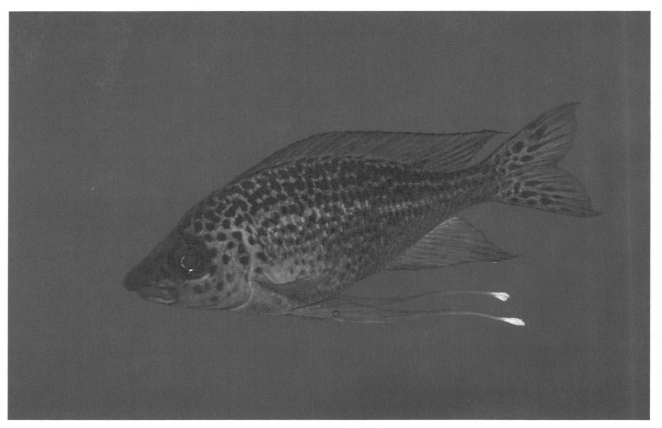

The specific name of this cichlid, *Ophthalmotilapia nasuta*, is an adjective meaning "having a (distinctive) nose" and ends according to the gender of the generic name, which is feminine. Photo taken in Moliro Bay, Zaïre.

after a M. Dubois. It enables us to refer to this species in the literature, and, to many of us, conjures up an immediate visual image derived from our own data banks. Sub-specific names allow us to identify distinct genetic groups within a species when such exist; they follow the same grammatical rules as specific names.

The specific name can be one of three types: an adjective (a descriptive word, eg "auratus", meaning "golden"); a genitive (the possessive of a name, eg "duboisi", which means "of Dubois"); or a noun in apposition (a noun used to qualify another noun, eg "Mr Bun the Baker", or, aquatically, *Pseudotropheus zebra, "Cichlasoma" centrarchus*).

The commonest type of Latin adjective has the "-us", "-a", "-um" endings (respectively masculine, feminine, neuter) mentioned earlier in respect of nouns; there is another common type with the endings "-is" (masculine and feminine) and "-e" (neuter), eg *Apistogramma pertensis, "Cichlasoma" nicaraguense*. It is worth noting in passing that in Latin ALL syllables are pronounced, and that the correct pronounciation of the "ense" ending is "en-say" (two syllables)!

Adjectival specific names MUST agree in gender with the generic name to which they are applied, and so if the species is moved from one genus to another, with an attendant change of gender, the specific name must be altered. Thus *Cichlasoma severum* (neuter) is now *Heros severus* (masculine).

A genitive is the possessive form of a Latin noun, and is equivalent to "of X" in English. In taxonomy it is almost always used to name a species after a person, although there are rare exceptions —*Tanganicodus irsacae* is named for the organisation IRSAC, and *Tangachromis dhanisi* after a boat, the "Baron von Dhanis". Although as a rule adjectives are used to denote place names, occasionally the genitive of such a name is used, usually where it is impossible to form a sensible adjective, as with African names such as Nkhata and Nkamba.

Genitives take the gender of their originator, with the masculine ending "-i" ("regani", "burtoni"), and feminine "-ae" ("kingsleyae", "trewavasae"). The feminine ending has also been used in the place name derivatives "nkatae" and "nkambae" for reasons of common sense and pronounciation*.

Very very occasionally a species is named after two people, thus we have *"Cichlasoma" hogaboomorum*, named for the Hogaboom brothers, "-orum" being the masculine plural ending. The feminine equivalent is "-arum", but I

Tanganicodus irsacae is named after an organisation. Photo taken near Kavalla Island, Zaïre.

can think of no example of its use.

Genitives are thus quite distinctive, and unlikely to be confused with adjectives. They remain constant whatever the gender of the generic name.

Unfortunately nouns in apposition often have "-us", "-a", "-um" endings like some adjectives, and when the species involved are moved to a different genus it is all too common for these names to be subjected to "blanket" gender changing by aquarists. But because they are nouns in their own right they have their own gender, which always remains the same whatever the generic name. Some are easy to spot, especially where they are the names of other animals —the derivation of *Pseudotropheus zebra* is obvious to everyone; if you know that *Centrarchus* is the name of another genus which *"Cichlasoma" centrarchus* resembles then there is no problem. But there are also "ordinary" nouns used in apposition, and, to exacerbate matters, some of these are themselves composites of a noun and adjective. "Melanotheron" ("black-chin") and "curviceps" ("curved-head") will probably be left well alone, but the same cannot be said for "maculicauda" ("spotted-tail") or "longimanus" ("long-hand" [-fin]) which look like adjectives but are not. Life becomes even more confusing when one realises that there is a perfectly good adjective "maculicaudatus, -a, -um" ("having a spotted tail") which must agree with any generic name to which it is applied.

It must be quite obvious, from the above, that without a lot of background knowledge, either of Latin and Greek vocabulary, or of taxonomic literature, the average aquarist cannot hope correctly to revise every specific name where generic change has occurred. In consequence it is wise to conduct a little research before committing oneself to paper or in public.

Recently some authors have adopted the practice of explaining the derivations and genders of the names they create; many earlier authors, however, omit to provide any derivation, and gender/grammar are not even mentioned as these used to be a matter of common knowledge amongst scientists, who, until comparatively recently, would automatically have received a "classical education". In the absence of any clues in the original description it can be helpful to examine the subsequent synonymy of a species, as any earlier variation in the specific name will usually point to an adjective. The *"Cichlid Catalogue"* of Ufermann, Allgayer, and Geerts (1987) can be extremely helpful for this purpose.

Doubtless many aquarists will question whether there is any point in going to all this trouble.

Well, the point of any language, taxonomic or otherwise, is to make oneself understood, and the trinomial system is intended to facilitate the communication of species identity between people of different languages. If it is to fulfil this purpose then it needs to be used accurately and precisely. And, in an era where scientists are beginning to take notice of observations made by aquarists, it is important for our credibility that we too are precise and accurate if we wish to make a meaningful contribution to the knowledge of our cichlids.

References

KULLANDER, S.O. (1980) A taxonomical study of the genus *Apistogramma* Regan, with a revision of Brazilian and Peruvian species (Teleostei: Percoidei: Cichlidae). *Bonn. Zool. Monog.* 14: 22.

UFERMANN, A., ALLGAYER, R., and GEERTS, M. (1987) *Cichlid Catalogue.* Brumath, France. ISMN 2-9502193-0-6.

* For many years there has been confusion over the genitive form of the name Moore (referring to J.E.S. Moore, collector of the type species of the genus *Tropheus*). Boulenger's original description uses *moorii*, being the genitive of the latinised form "Moorius" of Moore's name; some authors maintain that "moorei", a simple genitive of the English form, should be used. If, however, we refer to the rules of zoological nomenclature we find that there is no room for dispute. Any author describing a new species can choose whether he latinises a name before using it, or simply applies the appropriate ending. It is not for subsequent authors to question his decision. The name published in the original description of a taxon is the correct one (provided, of course, that there is no question of synonymy, preoccupation, or gender change). A name can be altered only if it was mis-spellt by the typist or printer (but NOT if the mistake was the author's) or if it is grammatically incorrect. None of these apply in Boulenger's case, so his published name *Tropheus moorii* is the correct one.

Spawning techniques in mouthbrooders
1. Fertilization in mouthbrooding cichlids

Dr. Ethelwynn Trewavas

Wickler (1962a,b) put forward two theories to explain the evolution of the egg-mimicking spots on the anal fin of males of many mouth-brooding haplochromines:

1. that they served to trigger spawning in the female, and

2. that the female, who has taken the eggs into her mouth very rapidly as they are laid, is tricked into trying to pick up the egg-dummies and so to inhale sperm from the male's vent and to ensure the oral fertilization of any eggs not already fertilized.

These theories have been widely accepted, but recently they have been challenged by Eva Hert (1989). Hert's experiments showed that the spots in *A. elegans* attract and stimulate the female, although only if accompanied by courting movements of the male. The fertilization rate, however, was not significantly different between males with egg-spots and those from which the spots had been removed by freeze-branding, both achieving nearly 100%.

Comparison of experimental with natural conditions

The experimental conditions were: one male and five females were together isolated in each of 12 separate compartments. There were thus no rival males, no predators, no egg-robbers, no water currents. These are ideal conditions for undisturbed spawning. In contrast abundant evidence exists that in nature a spawning pair may be surrounded by any or all of these hazards (see McKaye, 1983; Ribbink *et al.* 1983; Konings, 1989: 291; 1990: 150, 204).

Adaptation to mouthbrooding

Mouthbrooding has evolved several times in the family Cichlidae, in its most advanced form in the tribes Tilapiini and Haplochromini (Peters & Berns, 1978 and 1979). The tilapiines include both substrate- and mouth-brooders. Evolution from the former to the latter involved the regression and loss of features adaptive to substrate-spawning and guarding, and the development of new features appropriate to the care of larger and fewer, non-adhesive eggs. The problem was, how to get the eggs rapidly into the maternal mouth without neglecting their fertilization. Meeting this need there evolved a behavioural trait, first described by Baerends & Baerends-Van Roon (1950: fig. 50, 51) and named "tail-chasing" (Fryer, 1959), T-positions (Heinrich, 1967), making half-loops (Balon, 1977) or "tight circles" (Kapralski, 1990b) with each other. The alternating T-positions are: TA: male's snout contacts female's body near the vent, TB: male places his body before the female with his vent near her mouth. The series of T-positions culminates after a very short time or up to 30 min. (Berns *et al.*, 1978) in the "real spawning", when at TA the female lays an egg or a batch of eggs and at TB she collects them, either allowing the male to fertilize them first or more rapidly so that she has to inhale the sperm to fertilize them in her mouth.

It is this last movement, oral fertilization, that Wickler suggested was prompted by the deception of the egg-mimics on the male's anal fin in species possessing them.

A pair of *Copadichromis eucinostomus* (Msuli Point, 16 m) displaying the TB-position; see text for explanation.

The series of T-positions (TA-TB-TA-TB) is repeated until the female has no more eggs to lay. The importance of circling with T-positions is that by mutual stimulation it synchronises the spawning acts of male and female and facilitates fertilization either immediately before, during or after the collection of the eggs (Mrowka, 1987).

Wickler's prime exemplar of oral fertilization was *Astatotilapia* (formerly *Haplochromis*) *burtoni*. His film of this species shows the female making over the "egg-dummies" the same lip-movements that, immediately before, she has used to suck in the real eggs. Descriptions of spawning in mbuna by careful aquarists give the same picture, e.g. Mary Bailey (letter of 28-1-1989) describes the apparent efforts of *Pseudotropheus socolofi* to suck in the eggsspots as "persistent". Wickler used the word "energisch" for the same behaviour in his *"H. wingatii"* (the species Wickler studied was *Astatotilapia* cf. *bloyetii* from Tanzania).

The female *"H. wingatii"*, however, sometimes gives the male time to fertilize the eggs before she collects them. In that case she "does not deem the spots worth a glance" (Wickler, trans. E.T.). This indicates that when she does take an interest in the fin her behaviour is directed to fertilization rather than to egg-safety. Wickler's theory, on the other hand, distinguishes between the female's probable motive (safety) and the survival-value of her action (fertilization).

It is evident that *"H. wingatii"* is flexible in its technique, as, in response to environmental situations, some other species are found to be (Konings, this vol. p. 97). *A. burtoni* seems to be more rigid in its use of oral fertilization. Paulo's experiment (1975) with this species, in which he removed a male's anal fin, clearly shows that the egg spots, and even the fin itself, are not necessary for oral fertilization. This cannot be deduced from Hert's results because we do not know whether *A. elegans* used oral fertilization either during the experiment or otherwise.

The use of similar lip-movements over eggs and "egg-dummies" which seemed to support Wickler's theory, is weakened as evidence when we realise that the same method, namely suction, would be used for taking in either eggs or sperm. At this time the fin is probably covered with sperm.

Occurrence of egg-spots

Tilapiine mouthbrooders and some haplochromines have no bright yellow spots on the anal fin of males. Many Malawian species have a conspicuous pattern, usually yellow, that does not resemble eggs, but in mbuna and some others the orange to orange-yellow spots are surrounded by a contrasting border or a dark fin and have been called egg-spots. The closest resemblance between spots and eggs characterises the haplochromines of the Lakes Victoria, Edward, and Kivu (VEK) group and related species of streams, lagoons and the inshore waters of lakes, e.g. *A. burtoni* and *A. calliptera*. In these the spots are of the same order of size as the eggs and resemble them in colour and shape (Goldschmidt, 1991). The contrasting border is well-marked and regular (or the fin itself is dark). Their mimicry has been accepted even by some who reject Wickler's explanation of it. Among the mbuna there are some with a pattern indistinguishable from this type, others in which the spots are much smaller and arranged in a cluster instead of in rows. Occasionally they may occur also on the dorsal fin or in females. There is interspecific variation as well as a degree of uniformity within a species or a population (Konings, 1990 and pers. comm.). This gives some support to the theory of Axelrod (see Ribbink in Jackson & Ribbink, 1975) that the female recognizes the species-specific pattern. This theory and that of Konings (1989, p. 29) that the displayed anal fin, especially when bearing a brightly coloured pattern, "shows the female where to spawn" are applicable both to patterns not resembling eggs and to egg-spots. Neither claims any influence of the spots on oral fertilization.

Oral fertilization without egg-spots

For haplochromines see Konings, this vol. p. 97.

Fertilization in maternal mouthbrooding tilapiines has been described for seven species among the three subgenera of *Oreochromis*. These accounts are summarized in Trewavas, 1983 (pp. 190, 367, 387, 419, 450, 475, 487), where references to the original records are supplied. In six species oral fertilization is inferred from the snapping actions of the female close to the genital papilla of the male during the laying and collecting of the eggs. The seventh species, *O. (Nyasalapia) karomo*, was observed in the Malagarazi Swamps, where male and female glided successively over the nest evidently laying and fertilizing the eggs. Similar behaviour by *O. macrochir* was seen in the Lufira River, but in the laboratory the female mouthed the genital tassel of the male. Wickler suggested that the tassel might function as a kind of spermatophore. If so, it would be by retaining the spermatic fluid (slightly more viscous than water) at the surface of its branches long enough for the female to obtain a concentration of sperm. The male's genital pore is at the base of the bifid tassel (see Trewavas, 1983, fig. 171).

Astatotilapia calliptera, Thumbi East, L. Malaŵi. The perfect egg-mimics. Note their position. See also photos on pp 54-57.

Aulonocara sp. "Chitande Type Masinje". A lavish display on a black fin. Photos by Ad Konings.

Petrochromis sp., Bulu Point, L. Tanganyika. Egg-spots on both anal and dorsal fins. Photo by Walter Dieckhoff.

The tassel in all species of this subgenus (*Nyasalapia*) is cream- to orange-coloured in contrast to the usually black breeding colour of the male. The black male of *O. mossambicus* has a prominent yellow papilla. In *O. (Alcolapia) alcalica grahami* the white papilla is surrounded by a black ring, which is highly conspicuous on the white skin of the belly as shown in a photograph by Dr. Wickler in Albrecht *et al.* (1968), also reproduced in Trewavas, 1983. As Fryer & Iles (1972) note, conspicuousness is an

attribute shared by these features and the decorated anal fin of haplochromines. See also Goldschmidt (1991), who seems to rate it as at least as important as the mimetic nature of the egg-spots.

As food for thought on this subject I call attention to two published photos. One, by Spreinat (1990: 529), shows a pair of *Rhamphochromis* sp. in an early stage of courtship. The body and fins are of uniform colour, except the male's anal fin, which bears a conspicuous yellow pattern. The female is targetting this fin. The second is a photo, by Milner, on p. 4 of Jackson & Ribbink (1975), of a group of partial albino *Pseudotropheus zebra*. These have no dark pigment —even the retina shows pink through the pupil— but in three individuals the anal fin bears a cluster of 2-4 small orange-yellow spots in a black field. Nothing could be more conspicuous or less egg-like. What genetic quirk has here made an exception in favour of the most valuable asset of a male cichlid?

Summary and conclusions

In maternal mouthbrooding cichlids fertilization, especially oral fertilization, is facilitated by various means. Mutual circling with T-positions ensures insemination either during or after collection of the eggs. The female is guided to the location of the male's genital papilla by a conspicuous device, —the colour of the papilla in contrast with its surroundings, an outgrowth of the papilla (rosette or tassel) or a conspicuous pattern on the male's anal fin. It is suggested that the tassel or fin delays the dispersion of the somewhat viscous seminal fluid and that it is for this that the female mouths tassel or fin at the end of a spawning bout if she still holds unfertilized eggs in her mouth.

This theory of the female's interest in the male's fin does not differentiate between the egg-pattern and any other, and causes us to look again at Wickler's second theory. An emergency that causes the female to pick up the eggs unfertilized may also cause her concern for egg-safety to amount to an obsession and make her more easily deceived by the egg-dummies. Some studies of fertilization already show that behaviour in this function may be influenced by the environmental situation (see Kapralski, 1990a and c) and more such studies are desirable, using species with different anal-fin patterns. The egg-pattern appears to be very successful, since it occurs in all species of *Astatotilapia* and related genera constituting the VEK group of haplochromines as well as several species of the more diverse flock of Lake Malawi and some of Lake Tanganyika. Wickler's two theories are the only ones that offer an explanation of its evolution and they have so far not been disproved. Unless at least one of them is accepted, then I doubt if we are justified in giving the resemblance the name of egg mimicry. After all, it is a very simple shape and the dark border that gives the spots a three-dimensional appearance also makes them very conspicuous, a valuable asset. The theory of mimicry must rest on the supposition that the egg-image has a special significance for the gravid female, and this has not been disproved.

Cost-benefit estimate

It has been objected (Konings, 1989: 30) that the conspicuously decorated anal fin may carry the disadvantage of attracting predators, especially when the spots are egg-mimics. This is a special case of a dilemma very common throughout the vertebrates. Evolution seems to have decided that the benefit of successful breeding outweighs the possible cost. This is why both we and the peahen can enjoy the display of the peacock, and why both female cichlids and fish photographers are seduced by the brilliant colours of male cichlids.

Acknowledgements

I have benefitted by discussions with Dr. Tijs Goldschmidt and with aquarist friends, especially Mary Bailey and Ad Konings, as well as from their published works. I am grateful to my friend Mrs. Isabel Rampton for kindly typing the script.

References

ALBRECHT, H., APFELBACH, R. & WICKLER, W. (1968) Über die Eigenständigkeit der Art *Tilapia grahami* Boulenger, ihren Grubenbau und die Zucht in reinem Süßwasser (Pisces, Cichlidae) *Senckenberg. biol.* 49; pp 107-118.
BAERENDS, G.P. & BAERENDS-Van ROON, J.M. (1950) An introduction to the study of the ethology of cichlid fishes. *Behaviour suppl.* I. 243 pp.
BALON, E.K. (1977) Early ontogeny of *Labeotropheus* Ahl, 1927 (mbuna, Cichlidae, Lake Malawi) with a discussion on advanced protective systems in fish reproduction and development. *Env. Biol. Fish.* 2 (2); pp 147-176.
BERNS, S., CHAVE, E.H. and PETERS, H.M. (1978) On the biology of *Tilapia squamipinnis* (Günther) from Lake Malawi (Teleostei: Cichlidae). *Arch. Hydrobiol.* 84; pp 218-246.
FRYER, G. and ILES, T.D. (1972) *The Cichlid Fishes of the Great Lakes of Africa*. Oliver and Boyd, Edinburgh & London.
GOLDSCHMIDT, T. (1991) Egg mimics in haplochromine cichlids from Lake Victoria. *Ethology.* 88; pp 177-190.
GOLDSCHMIDT, T. & DE VISSER, J. (1990) On the possible role of egg-mimics in speciation. *Acta Bioth.* 38; pp 125-134.
HEINRICH, W. (1967) Untersuchungen zum sexualverhaltung der Gattung *Tilapia* (Cichlidae, Teleostei) und bei Artbastarden. *Z. Tierpsychol.* 24; pp 684-754.

HERT, E. (1989) The function of egg-spots in an African mouth-brooding cichlid fish. *Anim. Behav.* 37; pp 726-732.
JACKSON, P.B.N. & RIBBINK, A.J. (1975) *Mbuna.* TFH Publ., New Jersey. (Illustr. in colour) 128 pp.
KAPRALSKI, A. (1990a) Breeding *Pseudotropheus tropheops*. *TFH* June: pp 86, 89-92.
KAPRALSKI, A. (1990b) Spawning *Labeotropheus fuelleborni*. *TFH* July: pp 10-13, 17 illustr.
KAPRALSKI, A. (1990c) Breeding *Haplochromis compressiceps*. *TFH* August: pp 32-34, 37, 41.
KONINGS, A. (1989) *Lake Malawi cichlids in their natural habitat*. Verduijn Cichlids & Lake Fish Movies. Netherlands. 313 pp. illustr.
KONINGS, A. (1990) *Cichlids and all the other fishes of Lake Malawi*. TFH Publ. Neptune City, NJ. 495 pp. illustr.
McKAYE, K.R. (1983) Ecology and breeding behaviour of a cichlid fish, *Cyrtocara eucinostomus*, on a large lek in Lake Malawi, Africa. *Env. Biol. Fish.* 8; pp 81-98.
MROWKA, W. (1987) Oral fertilization in a mouth-brooding cichlid fish. *Ethology.* 74; pp 293-296.
PAULO, J. (1975) Bedeutung der Eiflecke. *DCG-Info* (German Cichl. Ass.) 6; pp 163-165.
PETERS, H.W. & BERNS, S. (1978) Über die Vorgeschichte der maulbrütenden Cichliden. 1. Was uns die Haftorganen der Larven lehren. pp 211-217. 2. Zwei Typen von Maulbrütern. pp 324-331. (illstr. in col.). *Aquarium Magazin*
PETERS, H.M. & BERNS, S. (1979) Regression und Progression in der Evolution maulbrütender Cichliden. *Mittl. Hamb. zool. Mus. Inst.* 76; pp 506-508.
RIBBINK, A.J., MARSH, B.A., MARSH, A.C., RIBBINK, A.C., and SHARP, B.J. (1983) A preliminary survey of the cichlid fishes of rocky habitats in Lake Malawi. *S. Afr. J. Zool.* 18 (3); pp 149-310.
SPREINAT, A. (1990) Beobachtungen an *Rhamphochromis*-Arten. *DATZ* 43; pp. 528-533.
TREWAVAS, E. (1983) *Tilapiine fishes of the genera Sarotherodon, Oreochromis and Danakilia.* 583p., London, Br. Mus. Nat. Hist.
WICKLER, W. (1962a) Zur Stammesgeschichte funktionell korrelierter Organ- und Verhaltensmerkmale: Ei-Attrappen und Maulbrüten bei afrikanischen Cichliden. *Z. Tierpsychol.* 19; pp 129-164.
WICKLER, W. (1962b) Egg-dummies as natural releasers in mouth-breeding cichlids. *Nature* 194; pp 1092-1093.
WICKLER, W. (1966) Über die biologischen Bedeutung des Genital-Anhangs der männlichen *Tilapia macrochir*. *Senckenberg biol.* 47; pp 419-422.

Pseudotropheus tropheops OB morph (Chinyamwezi Reef). The TA-position: the male's snout contacts the female's body near the vent while she deposits some eggs.

2. The spawning-techniques of Malaŵian haplochromines

Ad Konings

All the haplochromine species of Lake Malaŵi are maternal mouthbrooders. Usually spawning begins with the manoeuvre known as circling with alternating T-positions (TA-TB: see Trewavas, this vol. p. 93) which brings the pair to a synchronised spawning act when the eggs are laid, fertilized, and taken into the mouth almost simultaneously. While the female deposits the egg(s) the male has its head close to the female's vent (TA-position). This position is very characteristic for most mouthbrooders. All haplochromine mouthbrooders display the TB-position where the female collects the eggs and/or sperm. As Wickler (1962a) recorded for his *"H. wingatii"*, some species practise fertilization either before or after the female has picked up the eggs. Recent descriptions by Kapralski (1990) show that in some species behaviour is flexible in response to the environmental situation. I have observed that females collect the eggs more rapidly in a crowded situation than in a peaceful one.

The fertilization of the eggs outside the female's mouth (*external fertilization*) has now been recorded for several Malaŵian species, e.g. *Dimidiochromis compressiceps, Pseudotropheus* sp. "Tropheops Chilumba" (Kapralski, 1990c, 1990a), *Nimbochromis livingstonii, Cyrtocara moorii,* and *Labeotropheus trewavasae* (Konings, 1989). Most of these species are known to fertilize (partly) the eggs in the mouth as well, i.e. *D. compressiceps* (Knabe, pers. comm.), *Labeotropheus* spp. (Balon, 1977; Bailey, pers. comm.), *C. moorii* (De Langhe, Pers. comm.), *Ps. tropheops* (pers. obs.). It seems that these species practise an oral fertilization when they feel disturbed. We may call this technique the *"facultative oral fertilization".* It is not known whether these conditions are natural or induced by the confines of the aquarium. Many more species may practise an environmentally induced variation of fertilization.

So far, *N. livingstonii* is the only species of the group of which oral fertilization has not (yet) been observed.

It is therefore not enough to say "spawning by the usual haplochromine method". Moreover a second spawning variant (more advanced?), whereby the TA-position is not practised, has been described (see Konings, 1989).

This second technique is employed by (probably) a large group of non-mbuna. I have observed it in *C. borleyi, Maravichromis lateristriga, Protomelas taeniolatus* and *Copad.* sp. "Kawanga". During the entire spawning act the male never has its head near the female's vent (TA-position). In order to bring the pair to a synchronized spawning act the male leads the female to the spawning-site where an initial TB-position culminates in a circling around each other. After a few rounds the male discontinues the circling. While the female discharges her eggs the male waits beside her (passively?) until she has collected the eggs in her mouth. Then he circles her again and quivers his anal fin over the nest. Although quivering, the male does not move forward but probably exudes its semen. The female snaps at the male's vent and probably inhales the milt to fertilize the eggs inside her mouth. We may call this spawning technique the *"total oral fertilization"* method as all eggs are fertilized inside the female's mouth.

Of the three fertilization techniques mentioned the facultative oral fertilization method is the one most commonly observed in the aquarium. Facultative and total oral fertilization have both been observed in the natural environment (pers. obs.: *Ps. zebra* and *Ps.* sp. "Elongatus Ornatus", and *Copad.* sp. "Kawanga" respectively).

For references see page 96.

Acknowledgements

I gratefully acknowledge the discussions I enjoyed with Dr. Ethelwynn Trewavas about many aspects of cichlid-ichthyology and with Gerard Tijsseling and Peter Baasch about spawning behaviour in cichlids.

A pair in TB-position. Note the egg near the anal fin.

The "total oral fertilization" method is practised by *C. borleyi.*

CICHLID ORGANIZATIONS WORLDWIDE

Australia
The New South Wales Cichlid Society
P.O. Box 163
Moorebank, N.S.W. 2170

Queensland Cichlid Group
P.O. Box 163
Wooloongabba, Queensland 4102

Victorian Cichlid Society
23 Mangana Drive
Mulgrave, Victoria 3170

Austria
Deutsche Cichliden Gesellschaft
Victor Kaplan Straße 1-9/1/3/12
A-1220 Wien

Belgium
Belgische Cichliden Vereninging
Kievitlaan 23
B-2228 Ranst

Czechoslovakia
SZCH Klub Chovatelov Cichlíd
Príkopova 2
CS-831 03 Bratislava

Denmark
Dansk Cichlide Selskab
Ornevej 58, st. tv.
DK-2400 Kobenhavn NV

France
Association France Cichlid
15 Rue des Hirondelles
F-67350 Dauendorf

Germany
Deutsche Cichliden Gesellschaft
Eberescheweg 41
D(W)-4200 Oberhausen

Hungary
Hungarian Cichlid Association
Lukács László, Karolina út 65
H-1113 Budapest

Netherlands
Nederlandse Cichliden Vereniging
Boeier 31
NL-1625 CJ Hoorn

Sweden
Nordiska CiklidSällskapet
Skogsgläntan 16
S-435 38 Mölnlycke

Switzerland
Deutsche Cichliden Gesellschaft
Am Balsberg 1
CH-8302 Kloten

Taiwan (R.O.C.)
Taiwanese Cichlid Association
N°17, Lane 239, An-Ho Road
Taipei

United Kingdom
British Cichlid Association
100 Keighley Road
Skipton, North Yorkshire, BD23 2RA

British Cichlasoma Study Group
93 Banks Lane
Offerton, Stockport SK1 4JK

U. S. A.
American Cichlid Association
P.O. Box 32130
Raleigh, NC 27622

Adv. Cichl. Aquarists South California
P.O. Box 8173
San Marino, CA 91108

Apistogramma Study Group
1845 Jaynes Road
Mosinee, WI 54455

Cichlasoma Study Group
6432 South Holland Court
Littlerton, CO 80123

Fort Wayne Cichlid Association
9638 Manor Woods Rdf.
Ft. Wayne, IN 46804

Greater Chicago Cichlid Association
2633 N. Rhodes
River Grove, IL 60171

Greater Cincinnati Cichlid Association
15 W. Southern Avenue
Covington, KY 41015

Illinois Cichlids and Scavengers
7807 Sunset Drive
Elmwood Park, IL 60635

Michigan Cichlid Association
P.O. Box 59
New Baltimore, MI 48047

Ohio Cichlid Association
3896 Boston Rd.
Brunswick, OH 44212

Pacific Coast Cichlid Association
P.O. Box 28145
San Jose, CA 95128

Rocky Mountain Cichlid Association
5065 W. Hinsdale Cir.
Littleton, CO 80123

Southern California Cichlid Association
P.O. Box 574
Midway City, CA 92655

Texas Cichlid Association
6845 Winchester
Dallas, TX 75231